VIDEO WORKSHEETS

COPYMASTERS AND ANSWER KEY

Fabián A. Samaniego
University of California, Davis
Emeritus

M. Carol Brown
California State University, Sacramento

Patricia Hamilton Carlin
University of Central Arkansas, Conway

Sidney E. Gorman
Fremont Unified School District
Fremont, California

Carol L. Sparks
Mt. Diablo Unified School District
Concord, California

McDougal Littell
Evanston, Illinois • Boston • Dallas

Printed in the United States of America

International Standard Book Number: 0-669-43368-3

2 3 4 5 6 7 8 9 10   BA   99 98

CONTENIDO

LECCIÓN PRELIMINAR   LP

00:00 – 01:56

Side 1, 9 to 3500

PARA EMPEZAR

A. Orden numérico. The detective sees several scenes in the classroom. Listen to the video carefully. Then number the scenes shown below in the order in which the detective finds them in the classroom.

a. _____

b. _____

c. _____

B. Detective. Listen to the video carefully. Then indicate which items the detective finds in the **mochila (M)**, on the **escritorio (E)**, or in the **clase (C)**. Some items have more than one correct answer.

_____ mochila   _____ pizarra

_____ pupitre   _____ lápiz

_____ libro de español   _____ escritorio

_____ bolígrafo   _____ mesa

_____ carpeta   _____ regla

_____ cuaderno   _____ silla

_____ tiza   _____ borrador

C. Ventana cultural: Dos culturas.   The video for this **Para empezar** was shot in a school in Puerto Rico. Which of the items pictured in the video are present in your own classroom? Write an **X** by each item present in both the Puerto Rican classroom and your classroom.

_____ tiza   _____ silla

_____ pizarra   _____ lápiz

_____ bolígrafo   _____ libro de español

_____ pupitre   _____ mochila

_____ borrador   _____ carpeta

_____ regla   _____ cuaderno

_____ mesa   _____ escritorio de profesor

¿QUÉ DECIMOS...?

02:01

Side 1, 3639 to 5409

A. ¿Qué hay en la lista? On Armando's list, write the items that you hear in the conversation between Juan and Armando.

B. Ventana cultural: Dos culturas. Armando bought his school supplies in this bookstore in San Juan, Puerto Rico. What else did you see in the bookstore, besides the items he bought?

_____

_____

_____

Where would you buy these items in the United States?

_____

_____

_____

UNIDAD 1

CULTURAL MONTAGE:
Montebello, California

How does Montebello High School compare to your school?
For each category below, write one or two words to describe
Montebello High School and your school.

To play the montage, use barcode
or counter:

| 03:06 | – | 03:47 |

Side 1, 5655 to 6884

	Montebello High School	**Your School**
Buildings	_____	_____
	_____	_____
Students	_____	_____
	_____	_____
Teachers	_____	_____
	_____	_____
Signs	_____	_____
	_____	_____

LECCIÓN 1

To play **Para empezar** from start to finish, use barcode or counter:

| 03:47 | – | 06:23 |

Side 1, 6900 to 11601

PARA EMPEZAR

A. Saludos y despedidas. Are these people greeting each other or saying good-bye? Write **S (saludo)** or **D (despedida)** under the appropriate photos.

1. _____

2. _____

3. _____

4. _____

5. _____

B. ¿Quiénes son? As you meet the people in the video, draw a line connecting the photo of the person and the appropriate description.

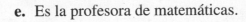

a. Es una estudiante.

b. Es un chico.

c. Es el profesor de historia.

d. Es la profesora de español.

e. Es la profesora de matemáticas.

f. Es el director de la escuela.

g. Dice, "Buenas noches, señor Ramos".

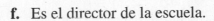

C. ¡Hola! How would the people in the photos greet each other: with a kiss on the cheek (**un besito**) or a handshake (**darse la mano**)? Mark the appropriate column with an **X**.

	un besito	**darse la mano**

1.    1. ☐   ☐

2.    2. ☐   ☐

3.    3. ☐   ☐

4.   4. ☐   ☐

5.    5. ☐   ☐

D. ¿Qué dice? As you listen carefully to the video, write in the missing
words to complete these descriptions.

1. ¿Quién es ella? Es Ana, una _____.

2. Es la profesora de _____, la señorita Montero.

3. Es el señor Whitaker. Es el _____ de historia.

4. Es mi _____ Lupe.

5. Es el _____ de la escuela, el señor Ramos.

Now check and correct your spelling.

    amiga   **director**   **español**   **estudiante**   **profesor**

¿QUÉ DECIMOS...?

To play ¿Qué decimos? from start to finish, use barcode or counter:

06:24 – 09:21

Side 1, 11610 to 16911

A. ¿Cómo estás? As you listen to and watch the video, number these people in the order in which you hear their names the first time.

a._____ b._____ c._____ d._____ e._____ f._____ g._____

B. ¡A contestar! How do people respond to greetings? As you listen to the video, draw a line from each greeting to the response given.

Saludos

1. Soy Lupe García.

2. Bien, gracias, ¿y tú?

3. ¿Cómo está usted, señorita Montero?

4. Soy el profesor de historia.

5. Buenas noches, Andrés.

Respuestas

a. Buenas noches, señor Ramos.

b. Beto Chávez. Mucho gusto.

c. Soy Luisa Montero. Encantada.

d. Terrible. . . Fatal.

e. Bien, gracias.

C. ¡A charlar! As you listen to the video, fill in the missing words in the sentences below.

1. Muchas gracias.
_____ Lupe García.

2. Hasta luego, Beto. Y, mucho
_____.

3. Hola, Lupe. ¿_____
_____? ¿Cómo estás?

4. ¿Cómo está _____,
señorita Montero?

5. Soy Luisa Montero.
_____.

6. Adiós, Andrés.
_____.

Now check and correct your spelling.

encantada   gusto   hasta mañana   qué tal   soy   usted

D. ¿Qué tal? How would you ask each of the people listed below how he or she is doing? Mark with an **X** the question that you would ask.

	¿Cómo estás?	¿Cómo está usted?
1. Sra. León	☐	☐
2. Ana	☐	☐
3. your principal	☐	☐
4. your English teacher	☐	☐
5. your best friend	☐	☐
6. Beto	☐	☐
7. your cousin	☐	☐

LECCIÓN 2

To play **Para empezar** from start to finish, use barcode or counter:

| 09:22 | – | 11:11 |

Side 1, 16929 to 20218

PARA EMPEZAR

A. Soy de Ecuador. Silvia López is introduced to all the people pictured here on her first day at Montebello High School. Write the names of the people she meets under their photos.

1. _____

2. _____

3. _____

4. _____

B. Mucho gusto. Complete each conversation with the response that you hear in the video.

(1) _____, Silvia.

Señorita Montero, quiero presentarle a Silvia López.

(2) _____, profesora.

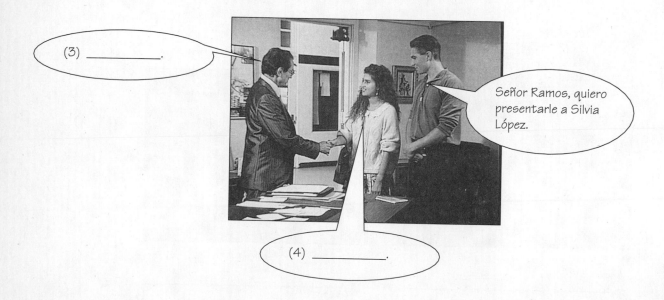

(3) _____.

Señor Ramos, quiero presentarle a Silvia López.

(4) _____.

Now check your spelling.

Es un placer.   **Igualmente.**   **Mucho gusto.**

C. ¿Presentarle o presentarte? How would you introduce Silvia to the people at Montebello High School? Circle the appropriate form in each sentence.

1. Señorita Montero, quiero (presentarle, presentarte) a Silvia López.

2. Jaime, quiero (presentarle, presentarte) a Silvia López.

3. Pilar, quiero (presentarle, presentarte) a Silvia López.

4. Sr. Whitaker, quiero (presentarle, presentarte) a Silvia López.

5. Sr. Ramos, quiero (presentarle, presentarte) a Silvia López.

6. Ana, quiero (presentarle, presentarte) a Silvia López.

¿QUÉ DECIMOS...?

A. Silvia es de Ecuador. As you listen to the video, indicate who makes each statement or asks each question by writing in the person's initial.

B (Beto)

S (Silvia)

A (Ana)

D (David)

R (Sr. Ramos)

M (Srta. Montero)

_____ **1.** David, quiero presentarte a Silvia López. Silvia es de Ecuador.

_____ **2.** Igualmente. Perdón, ¿cómo te llamas? ¿Ana?

_____ **3.** ¿De qué parte de Ecuador eres?

_____ **4.** El Sr. Ramos es el director de la escuela.

_____ **5.** Es un placer, Silvia. Bienvenida a Montebello High.

_____ **6.** Pero, ¡cuidado con Beto!

_____ **7.** ¡El gusto es mío, preciosa!

B. Quiero presentarte... As you listen to the video, draw a line from each sentence to the person who says it.

1. **a.** Quiero presentarte a Silvia López.

    b. Mucho gusto.

    c. El gusto es mío.

1.

2. **a.** ¿De qué parte de Ecuador eres?

    b. Soy de Quito.

2.

3. **a.** El Sr. Ramos es el director de la escuela.

    b. Mucho gusto.

    c. Es un placer. Bienvenida a Montebello High.

3.

C. Mucho gusto. How might Beto respond if he were introduced to the following people? Place an **X** under the response you think he would make.

	Mucho gusto.	**Encantado, preciosa.**
1. Ana	☐	☐
2. Sr. Ramos	☐	☐
3. David	☐	☐
4. Lupe	☐	☐
5. you	☐	☐
6. Silvia	☐	☐
7. your math teacher	☐	☐
8. the president's wife	☐	☐

Now compare your responses with those of three classmates.
Did you all agree?

LECCIÓN 3

To play **Para empezar** from start to finish, use barcode or counter:

| 13:54 | – | 16:25 |

Side 1, 25058 to 29644

PARA EMPEZAR

A. ¿Alta o baja? Watch and listen as students from Montebello are described. Mark with an **X** the words that are used to describe the girls.

☐ morena

☐ rubia

☐ pelirroja

☐ bonita

☐ fea

☐ cómica

☐ alta

☐ baja

☐ mediana

☐ gorda

☐ delgada

☐ atlética

☐ tímida

☐ popular

☐ elegante

☐ estudiosa

☐ inteligente

☐ tonta

☐ simpática

☐ antipática

B. ¿Quién es? Can you identify these people? Circle the photo of the
person who is being described in each sentence.

1.

   Gloria   Ángela   Carmen

   Es alta, morena y bonita.

2.

   Gloria   Ángela   Carmen

   No es ni alta ni baja, es mediana.

3.

   Gloria   Ángela   Carmen

   Es delgada, alta y atlética.

4.

   Carlos   Jaime

   Es alto, moreno y elegante.

5.

   Carlos   Jaime

   Es bajo y pelirrojo.

6.

   Carmen   Beto   Pirata

   Es muy simpático y
   muy, muy popular.

C. ¿Cómo es? Listen carefully to the video. As the following characters are introduced, mark an **X** by the words that are used to describe them.

Carmen	Jaime	Pirata
☐ morena	☐ moreno	☐ popular
☐ simpática	☐ estudioso	☐ feo
☐ baja	☐ alto	☐ bajo
☐ inteligente	☐ guapo	☐ tonto
☐ delgada	☐ cómico	☐ gordo
☐ alta	☐ elegante	☐ simpático

Now compare your lists with those of a classmate.

D. Ventana cultural: ¿Masculino o femenino? How would you describe Jaime and Ángela? Connect the appropriate adjectives with the person that they describe.

guapo   alto   morena   delgada   estudioso   mediana

atlética   rubio   moreno   bonita   delgado   alta

Now, in one or two sentences, describe Jaime or Ángela to a classmate. Listen while he or she describes the other person.

¿QUÉ DECIMOS...?

A. Es muy guapo. As you watch Pilar interview students, write the name of the person being described.

To play **¿Qué decimos?** from start to finish, use barcode or counter:

| 16:26 | – | 19:38 |

Side 1, 29647 to 35399

_____   **1.** Es muy guapo, inteligente y alto.

_____   **2.** Es flaco.

_____   **3.** Es nerviosa y tímida.

_____   **4.** Es alto y moreno.

_____   **5.** Es bonita, simpática y popular.

_____   **6.** Es grande, fuerte y guapo.

_____   **7.** Es estudioso.

B. ¡Entrevista! As you listen to the video, write in the missing descriptive words in the sentences below.

1.

Pues, soy alto y moreno. También soy muy _____.

2.

Mi amiga Lupe es muy bonita y muy _____.

3.

Francamente, soy bonita y _____ y muy popular

4.

Lupe, también eres muy _____, ¿no?

5.

Sí, Beto. Eres muy _____.

6.

¡No, no, no! Beto es _____, bajo y feo.

Now check and correct your spelling.

flaco   guapo   popular   modesta   simpática   tonto

© McDougal Littell, Inc.

C. ¿Cómo es? You have heard how students at Montebello describe themselves. How would you describe yourself? How would you describe the person sitting next to you? Write three or four adjectives to describe yourself. Then write three or four adjectives to describe the person next to you.

Yo	Mi amigo/amiga
_____	_____
_____	_____
_____	_____
_____	_____

Now compare your descriptions with those of the person sitting next to you.

D. Ventana cultural: Estudiantes de dos escuelas. Meet Esteban and Sara. They live in Puerto Rico and attend Robinson School. Would you describe them as being different from the students at Montebello High School, or would you describe them as being the same? Connect the descriptions below with the person or persons being described.

1. Es moreno.

2. Es morena.

3. Es americano.

4. Es simpática

Jaime

Ana

Esteban

Sara

5. Es estudioso.

6. Es delgada.

7. Es bonita.

8. Es flaco.

Compare your answers with those of a classmate. Did you agree?

UNIDAD 2

CULTURAL MONTAGE:
San Juan, Puerto Rico

To play the montage, use barcode or counter:

19:43 – 20:28

Side 2, 9 to 1382

1. Why, do you think, is there a statue of a Spanish explorer in San Juan?

_____

_____

2. **a.** What do you think the three flags over the yellow building in the video represent?

_____

_____

b. Why is there a flag of the United States of America?

_____

_____

3. In the Venn diagram below, write two or three similarities and two or three differences you observed between your city and San Juan.

Mi ciudad   **similar**   **San Juan**

_____   _____   _____

_____   _____   _____

_____   _____   _____

© McDougal Littell, Inc.

LECCIÓN 1

To play **Para empezar** from start to finish, use barcode or counter:

| 20:29 | – | 22:14 |

Side 2, 1402 to 4547

PARA EMPEZAR

A. ¿Qué clase tiene? While Esteban, Sara, Raúl, and Mónica talk about their classes, write the name of the appropriate class in each sentence.

| inglés | español | matemáticas | historia |
| educación | física | computación | |

1. Sara tiene la clase de _____ a las diez y media.

2. Esteban tiene _____ a las nueve y cinco.

3. Sara tiene _____ los lunes, miércoles y viernes.

4. Raúl tiene _____ con la Sra. Rodríguez.

5. Mónica y Sara van a estudiar _____ juntas.

B. Las clases. As you listen to the video, mark an **X** under the name of the student or students whose schedule is being described.

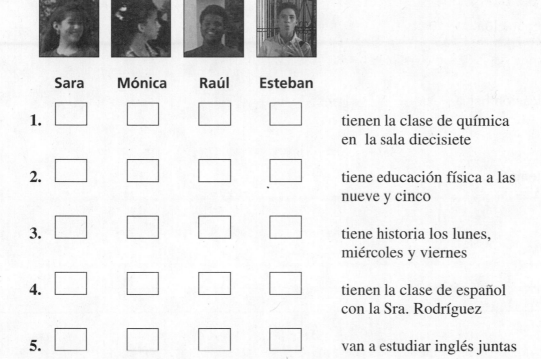

	Sara	Mónica	Raúl	Esteban
1.	☐	☐	☐	☐	tienen la clase de química en la sala diecisiete
2.	☐	☐	☐	☐	tiene educación física a las nueve y cinco
3.	☐	☐	☐	☐	tiene historia los lunes, miércoles y viernes
4.	☐	☐	☐	☐	tienen la clase de español con la Sra. Rodríguez
5.	☐	☐	☐	☐	van a estudiar inglés juntas

C. ¿A qué hora? The times for classes and activities of students at Robinson School may not be the same as for you. As you listen to the video, write the appropriate time in each sentence.

3:10   1:00   10:30   7:00   9:05   1:45

1. Esteban tiene educación física a las _____.

2. La clase de química es a las _____.

3. Sara tiene historia a la _____ los lunes, miércoles y viernes.

4. La clase de español con la Sra. Rodríguez es a las _____.

5. Las chicas estudian juntas a las _____.

D. Ventana cultural: Dos escuelas. In the video, you heard students talking about classes that they take at Robinson School. Are similar classes offered at your school? Mark an **X** next to the classes that are offered at both the Robinson School and at your school.

_____   computación

_____   educación física

_____   matemáticas

_____   inglés

_____   química

_____   historia

_____   español

_____   geografía

¿QUÉ DECIMOS...?

A. ¿Qué dice? Watch and listen to the conversations between Carlos and his classmates. Circle **sí** if Carlos or his friends say that Carlos takes these classes. Circle **no** if they do not say whether he takes these classes.

1. computación   sí   no

2. geografía   sí   no

3. historia   sí   no

4. inglés   sí   no

5. español   sí   no

6. educación física   sí   no

B. ¿Cuándo? Listen carefully to the video. Then draw a line to match each class with the correct times and days.

1. computación   **a.** 10:00; lunes, miércoles y viernes

2. geografía   **b.** 11:15; lunes, miércoles y viernes

3. inglés   **c.** 9:10; lunes, miércoles y viernes

4. educación física   **d.** 9:10; martes y jueves

C. ¿Qué pasa? As you listen to the students talk about their classes, indicate the correct completion for each sentence by circling the appropriate letter.

1. Carlos tiene la clase de computación con...

   a. Sara.

   b. Silvia.

2. Carlos tiene la clase de geografía a las...

   a. diez.

   b. once menos cuarto.

3. Carlos tiene educación física los...

   a. lunes, miércoles y viernes.

   b. martes y jueves

4. Carlos tiene educación física con...

   a. Sara.

   b. Raúl.

5. El número de teléfono de Carlos es el...

   a. 9–23–14–27

   b. 9–22–15–27

D. Ventana cultural: Números de teléfono. In the video, you heard Carlos give his telephone number in a form that is probably different from that which you are used to. Write your telephone number in the form that Carlos uses.

_____

Now ask three classmates for their telephone numbers and write them down along with their name.

¿Cuál es tu teléfono?

Nombre: _____ **Número:** _____

Nombre: _____ **Número:** _____

Nombre: _____ **Número:** _____

Have your friends check to see that you wrote their phone numbers correctly.

L E C C I Ó N 2

To play **Para empezar** from start to finish, use barcode or counter:

24:22 – 26:30

Side 2, 8375 to 12206

PARA EMPEZAR

A. La escuela Robinson. As you listen to Carmen and Raúl lead the tour of Robinson School, number the places below in the order in which they are mentioned in the video.

a. _____

b. _____

c. _____

d. _____

e. _____

B. ¿Cómo es la escuela? Carmen and Raúl are enthusiastic about their school. As they describe Robinson School, circle the appropriate word to complete each sentence below.

1. Robinson es un colegio (estupendo, fantástico).

2. La clase de español es (fantástica, divertida).

3. El profesor de español es (divertido, inteligente).

4. Las computadoras son (difíciles, nuevas) y las clases son populares.

5. Tengo unos amigos fantásticos, simpáticos, (exigentes, inteligentes) y divertidos.

6. Los experimentos de química son (serios, difíciles) pero interesantes.

7. Unos profesores son (serios, nuevos); otros son divertidos; otros son (estupendos, exigentes).

C. Mi escuela. With a partner, write four or five adjectives—in Spanish—
to describe your school, the students, and the teachers.

Mi escuela	Los estudiantes	Los profesores
_____	_____	_____
_____	_____	_____
_____	_____	_____
_____	_____	_____
_____	_____	_____

D. Ventana cultural: Las escuelas. You have listened to Raúl and Sara describe their
school. How would you describe your school? Mark an **X** before each of Raúl and Sara's
descriptions that matches your school.

Las clases son: _____ divertidas   y   _____ populares.

Los estudiantes son: _____ simpáticos   e   _____ inteligentes.

Los profesores son: _____ exigentes   y   _____ buenos.

Share what you have marked with a classmate. Do you agree?

¿QUÉ DECIMOS...?

A. La escuela Robinson. Listen carefully to the descriptions of the classes and teachers at Robinson School. Write **P (profesores)** before characteristics of professors that you hear mentioned, and write **C (clases)** before characteristics of classes.

To play **¿Qué decimos?** from start to finish, use barcode or counter:

| 26:31 | – | 28:33 |

Side 2, 12240 to 15885

1. _____ excelentes

2. _____ organizado

3. _____ fantásticas

4. _____ guapo

5. _____ simpática

6. _____ divertidas

7. _____ desorganizada

8. _____ estupenda

B. ¡A charlar! As you listen to the students in the video, complete their conversations with the appropriate word from the list.

biblioteca	gimnasio	excelentes	matemáticas
desorganizada	historia	fáciles	perfeccionista

1. **¿Dónde está?**

   Sara: Oye, ¿dónde está Carlos? ¿Está en el _____?

   Raúl: No. Creo que está en la _____.
   ¡Ah, mira! ¡Allí está!

   Carlos: ¿Por qué están ustedes aquí? Es el recreo. Vamos al patio.

2. **Somos muy simpáticos.**

   Sara: ¿Qué tal tus clases, Carlos?

   Carlos: Fantásticas. Pero no son _____.

   Sara: ¿Y los profesores?

   Carlos: Son _____.

3. **Es muy simpática.**

   Carlos: ¿Qué clase tienes ahora?

   Sara: _____ con la señora Estrada. Es una clase estupenda.

   Carmen: ¡Ay, no! Ella es tan _____.

   Sara: Sí, pero es muy simpática. Es una profesora muy buena y sus clases son muy divertidas.

4. **¡Es tan guapo!**

   Carmen: Ahora tengo _____ y el señor Arenas es mi profesor favorito.

   Sara: ¿Él, el _____ ? ¡Qué aburrido!

   Carmen: Aburrido, no. Es organizado y simpático. . . y es alto y muy guapo.

C. Ventana cultural: ¿Una persona o dos? Read the sentences below. Do they refer to one person or two? Draw a line from each question to the appropriate illustration.

dos personas

1. ¿Cómo están?

2. ¿Cómo estás?

3. ¿Por qué están aquí?

4. ¿Estás en la biblioteca?

5. ¿Qué clase tienes?

6. ¿Tienen la clase de geografía?

una persona

LECCIÓN 3

To play **Para empezar** from start to finish, use barcode or counter:

| 28:34 | – | 30:39 |

Side 2, 15911 to 19670

PARA EMPEZAR

A. ¿Qué hacen? What do students and teachers do on the weekends? As you listen carefully to the video, mark an **X** by the activities that you hear mentioned.

_____ estudiar	_____ ver la tele	_____ calificar exámenes
_____ comer pizza	_____ hablar por teléfono	_____ correr
_____ hacer la tarea	_____ salir	_____ hacer una comida
_____ limpiar la casa	_____ pasear en bicicleta	_____ alquilar una película
_____ bailar	_____ jugar básquetbol	_____ trabajar
_____ escribir cartas	_____ beber un refresco	_____ jugar tenis

B. Las actividades. Students and teachers are involved in many activities on the weekends. As you listen to the video, complete each sentence below with the appropriate word from the list.

alquilar	calificar	comer	correr	estudiar	hablar
hacer	jugar	limpiar	pasear	salir	preparar

1. **Srta. Rivera:**   Tengo que _____ exámenes.

2. **Carmen:**   Voy a _____ por teléfono…
   con Tomás.

3. **Tomás:**   Carlos y yo vamos a _____
   básquetbol.

4. **Tomás:**   Vamos a _____ pizza.

5. **Sr. Arenas:**   Voy a _____ la casa.

6. **Sra. Estrada:**   Voy a _____ una película.

C. ¿Quién hace la actividad? For each activity, mark an **X** under the character who is going to do it.

	Carmen	Tomás	Sr. Arenas
1. jugar básquetbol	☐	☐	☐
2. limpiar la casa	☐	☐	☐
3. pasear	☐	☐	☐
4. hablar por teléfono	☐	☐	☐
5. hacer una comida	☐	☐	☐
6. salir con una amiga	☐	☐	☐
7. comer pizza	☐	☐	☐

D. Ventana cultural: Actividades. The students at Robinson School engage in many activities on the weekend. Check each activity that you and your classmates also do on weekends.

_____ hacer la tarea

_____ jugar básquetbol

_____ salir con amigos

_____ hablar por teléfono

_____ estudiar

_____ correr

_____ comer pizza

_____ pasear en bicicleta

Do your classmates agree with your answers? Check with classmates who sit by you.

¿QUÉ DECIMOS...?

To play ¿Qué decimos? from start to finish, use barcode or counter:

| 30:40 | – | 33:01 |

Side 2, 19694 to 23925

A. ¿Quién? As you listen to the video, draw a line to the picture of the person who is going to do or has to do the activity listed.

Sara

Tomás

Mónica

Carlos

Raúl

Srta. Rivera

Carmen

1. Tiene que trabajar en el restaurante.
2. Tiene que estudiar matemáticas.
3. Va a salir con una amiga y va a pasear en bicicleta.
4. Va a hacer la comida y ver televisión.
5. Va a practicar el básquetbol.
6. Tiene que estudiar inglés.
7. Va a comer algo.

Sra. Estrada

B. ¿Actividad u obligación? Listen carefully to the video. Then write **A (actividad)** for an activity that the person *wants* to do, and **O (obligación)** for an activity that the person *has* to do.

_____ 1. Mónica: estudiar matemáticas

_____ 2. Carmen: pasear en bicicleta

_____ 3. La Srta. Rivera: limpiar la casa

_____ 4. La Sra. Estrada: ver televisión

_____ 5. El Sr. Arenas: correr

_____ 6. Raúl: estudiar inglés

_____ 7. Carlos: alquilar una película

_____ 8. Carlos: comer en el restaurante

C. ¿Y el profesor? With a partner, write three activities that you think your teacher has to do after school today.

_____

_____

_____

Now share your list with another pair of classmates.
Did any of your answers coincide?

D. Tus actividades. When do you do various activities? On the calendar, write any activities that you do, on the day you do them. You may do several activities on one day and you may do an activity several times during the week. Then write **A** (**actividad**) for those that you want to do, and **O** (**obligación**) for those that you have to do. When you have finished, compare your weekly activities with a partner.

LUNES	MARTES	MIÉRCOLES	JUEVES	VIERNES	SÁBADO	DOMINGO

E. Ventana cultural: Letreros. In the video, you saw several signs.
What do you think the signs below mean? What would similar signs in
your city look like? Sketch what the sign would be like where you live.

	Meaning	**In my city**

1.

_____

_____

_____

2.

_____

_____

_____

UNIDAD 3

CULTURAL MONTAGE:
México, D.F., México

To play the montage, use barcode or counter:

| 00:00 | – | 00:44 |

Side 3, 20 to 1351

1. What is distinctive about the taxis in Mexico City?

_____

_____

_____

_____

2. The **Museo Nacional de Antropología** is one of the most outstanding museums in the world. What would you expect to find there? With a partner, brainstorm four or five things that you might find in the museum.

_____

_____

_____

_____

_____

LECCIÓN 1

PARA EMPEZAR

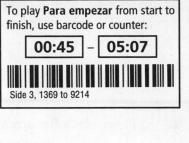

To play **Para empezar** from start to finish, use barcode or counter:

| 00:45 | – | 05:07 |

Side 3, 1369 to 9214

A. Lugares importantes. On the tour of Mexico City, you learn a lot about the city. As you listen carefully to the video, circle the word that correctly completes each sentence.

1. La Plaza Universidad es uno de los mejores (colegios / centros comerciales) de la capital.

2. El Ángel es el (monumento / palacio) a la independencia.

3. El Zócalo es (el mercado / la plaza) principal.

4. El Palacio de Bellas Artes es un (hotel / teatro) muy importante.

5. El Bosque de Chapultepec es el (palacio / parque) más grande de la capital.

6. En la Plaza Universidad hay (tiendas / monumentos) de toda clase.

B. ¿Cómo es? Watch and listen carefully to the video. Then write a word or phrase (in Spanish, if possible) that describes each of these places in Mexico City.

1. El Paseo de la Reforma

_____

_____

2. El Zócalo

_____

_____

3. El Palacio de Bellas Artes

_____

_____

4. El Bosque de Chapultepec

_____

_____

5. La Zona Rosa

_____

_____

C. Ventana cultural: Lugares importantes.

Which of Mexico City's landmarks that you saw in the video do you think
is most important to the Mexican people?

_____

_____

Why?_____

_____

_____

_____

_____

In groups of four, discuss your answers.

¿QUÉ DECIMOS...?

To play **¿Qué decimos?** from start to finish, use barcode or counter:

| 05:08 | – | 08:14 |

Side 3, 9243 to 14816

A. ¿Quién es? As you watch the video, identify the characters below by writing their names under their photos.

1. _____

2. _____

3. _____

4. _____

5. _____

6. _____

B. ¿Cierto o falso? As you listen to the conversations, mark whether each statement below is **C (cierto)** or **F (falso)**.

C   F   **1.** La familia Chávez va al parque el sábado.

C   F   **2.** Los discos están en oferta en Plaza Universidad.

C   F   **3.** Kati es mexicana.

C   F   **4.** Papá está en el parque con Riqui.

C   F   **5.** Alicia y Kati van al parque con la familia.

C   F   **6.** A Kati le encantan las películas en español.

© McDougal Littell, Inc.

C. ¡A charlar! In the video, Alicia has conversations with several people. As you watch and listen to the video, connect the excerpts from her conversation with the person to whom she is speaking.

1.

Bueno, los sábados voy al parque con mi familia. ¿Por qué?

¡Ay! ¿Por qué no vamos de compras? Mañana los discos están en oferta en Plaza Universidad.

4.

Voy de compras con mi amiga Kati.

¿La chica norteamericana?

2.

Kati, mi amiga norteamericana, va de compras a Plaza Universidad y me gustaría ir con ella.

Pues, yo creo que está bien, pero habla con tu papá. Está en el patio con Riqui.

3.

Es que mañana hay muchas ofertas en las tiendas y... me gustaría ir de compras.

¿De compras? ¿Mañana? Bueno, está bien.

D. Ventana cultural: El sábado. After watching and listening to Alicia's conversation with Kati and with her family, answer the following questions.

1. What is the usual Saturday afternoon activity of the Chávez family?

   _____

   _____

2. Why do you think they would do this every Saturday?

   _____

   _____

   _____

3. Do you and your family have an activity that you do every weekend? If so, what is it? Why do you do this?

   _____

   _____

   _____

   _____

LECCIÓN 2

PARA EMPEZAR

To play **Para empezar** from start to finish, use barcode or counter:

| 08:15 | – | 11:36 |

Side 3, 14839 to 20883

A. ¿Cuándo? As you listen carefully to the video, indicate if each of the following is **C (cierto)** or **F (falso)**.

C   F   **1.** En el verano

.

C   F   **2.** En la primavera

.

C   F   **3.** En el otoño

.

C   F   **4.** En el invierno

.

C   F   **5.** En el invierno

.

B. El tiempo en la Ciudad de México. Draw a line from each weather expression to the appropriate season. Remember that these are descriptions of weather in Mexico City.

1. Hace sol.

2. Llueve.

3. Hace buen tiempo.

4. Hace calor.

5. Por la mañana hace fresco y por la noche hace frío.

a. primavera

b. otoño

c. invierno

d. verano

C. Ventana cultural: El Bosque de Chapultepec. In the video, you
saw many aspects of Chapultepec Park. With a partner, answer the
questions below.

1. What animals did you see in the zoo in Chapultepec Park?

   _____

   _____

2. Would you prefer to go on the rides that Riqui goes on or the rides that
   Daniel goes on?

   _____

   Why?_____

   Is there an amusement park located near you that has these rides?

   _____

3. Outside one of the museums is a huge stone statue of Tlaloc,
   the rain god. Which museum would you visit to see this statue?

   _____

4. Which of these activities can you do in Chapultepec Park? Mark an **X**
   next to those activities.

   ☐ visitar el Museo Nacional
     de Antropología

   ☐ mirar los animales

   ☐ subir a la montaña rusa

   ☐ visitar el Museo deTecnología

   ☐ subir a las lanchas

   ☐ correr

   ☐ caminar por el Zócalo

5. Is there another activity that you and your partner would like to do
   there? Write it in Spanish.

   _____

¿QUÉ DECIMOS...?

To play ¿Qué decimos? from start
to finish, use barcode or counter:

| 11:37 | – | 14:45 |

Side 3, 20907 to 26554

A. ¿Qué hace? After listening to and watching the video, write, in Spanish if possible, five to eight activities that people do in Chapultepec Park.

_____   _____

_____   _____

_____   _____

_____   _____

B. ¿Qué dice? Read the sentences below. As you listen carefully to the video, draw a line from the photo of each person to the activities he or she performs.

1. Sólo sube a los juegos infantiles.

2. Pasea por el hermoso Bosque de Chapultepec.

3. Dice: "Me encanta el Museo de Antropología".

4. Pasa mucho tiempo en el parque.

5. Camina, escucha la radio, toma un refresco y mira a la gente.

6. Va a subir a la montaña rusa.

© McDougal Littell, Inc.

C. ¿Yo? Who is the speaker referring to? Circle **yo** if the speaker is talking about something that she or he does, or **otra persona** if the speaker is talking about something that another person does.

1. ¿Visita usted los museos del parque?   yo   **otra persona**

2. Camino y escucho la radio, tomo un   yo   **otra persona**
   refresco y miro a la gente.

3. Voy a comprar un helado.   yo   **otra persona**

4. ¿Pasas mucho tiempo en el parque?   yo   **otra persona**

5. Descansa o escribe cartas.   yo   **otra persona**

6. Los espero aquí.   yo   **otra persona**

7. Sólo sube a los juegos infantiles.   yo   **otra persona**

D. Ventana cultural: ¿Adulto o chico? After watching and listening to the video, you should have an idea of the activities that an adult might prefer and those that a young person might prefer. Read the list of activities and decide whether Eloísa or Riqui would likely prefer each activity. Write each activity under the appropriate name.

descansar	visitar un museo	subir a la montaña rusa
escuchar la radio	comer un helado	mirar los animales
caminar por el parque	mirar la gente	leer un libro
escribir cartas	subir a las lanchas	

      Eloísa   **Riqui**

_____   _____

_____   _____

_____   _____

_____   _____

_____   _____

Now compare your answers with those of a classmate. Are there any activities that both an adult and a young person might enjoy?

LECCIÓN 3

PARA EMPEZAR

To play **Para empezar** from start to
finish, use barcode or counter:

| 14:46 | – | 17:50 |

Side 3, 26576 to 32104

A. Un fin de semana típico. Where are people going and
what are they doing on the weekend? As you watch the video,
circle the letter of the appropriate completion for each sentence.

1.

Mis amigas y yo charlamos mientras…

   a. salimos a caminar.

   b. tomamos algo en un café.

2.

Kati y Teresa siempre compran algo. Yo…

   a. compro algo también.

   b. nunca compro nada.

3.

El muchacho que trabaja en el restaurante es…

   a. muy guapo.

   b. mi hermano.

4.

Kati y Daniel . . .

   a. bailan muy bien, no?

   b. escuchan muy bien, no?

B. ¿Viernes, sábado o domingo? Read the sentences below. As you listen carefully to the video, circle **V** (**viernes**), **S** (**sábado**), or **D** (**domingo**) to indicate the day of the week the teenagers do these activities.

V   S   D   **1.** Martín lleva a Alicia a una discoteca.

V   S   D   **2.** Alicia, Teresa y Kati escuchan discos
y casetes o ven televisión.

V   S   D   **3.** Alicia y sus amigas toman algo en un café.

V   S   D   **4.** Comen en un restaurante al aire libre.

V   S   D   **5.** Kati, Alicia y Teresa van de compras.

V   S   D   **6.** La familia va a la iglesia.

V   S   D   **7.** Kati y Daniel bailan mucho.

C. Ventana cultural: El fin de semana. Listed below are some activities that Alicia, her family, and her friends do on the weekend. Place a check next to the activities that you do on those days, too.

viernes	sábado	domingo
_____ charlar con amigos	_____ ir de compras	_____ ir a la iglesia
_____ tomar algo en un café	_____ comprar algo	_____ pasear
_____ caminar	_____ comer al aire libre	_____ comer con la familia
_____ escuchar discos y casetes	_____ ir a una fiesta	_____ ir a la discoteca
_____ ver televisión	_____ bailar	

In groups of four, compare your answers. Do you all do the same activities? Do you think that Alicia's activities are typical of the activities of other Mexican youth? Why or why not?

¿QUÉ DECIMOS . . .?

A. ¿Sí o no? After watching and listening to what Alicia, Kati, and Daniel do on Saturday, answer the questions below by circling **Sí** or **No**.

1. ¿Mira Kati un disco compacto de Menudo?   Sí   No

2. ¿Van a entrar al cine los chicos?   Sí   No

3. ¿Es rica la pizza en el restaurante italiano en la Zona Rosa?   Sí   No

4. ¿Toman limonada en el restaurante?   Sí   No

5. ¿Hay una fiesta en casa de Martín?   Sí   No

6. ¿Bailan más en Estados Unidos que en México?   Sí   No

7. ¿A Daniel le es extraño salir a pie?   Sí   No

B. ¿Dónde? As you watch and listen to the video, mark an **X** in the appropriate column to indicate where Alicia and Kati do or see the following, in **el centro comercial, el restaurante,** or **la fiesta**.

	el centro comercial	el restaurante	la fiesta
1. el disco compacto de Menudo	☐	☐	☐
2. bailar	☐	☐	☐
3. un camarero	☐	☐	☐
4. mucha gente	☐	☐	☐
5. hablar con David y Martín	☐	☐	☐
6. una pizza	☐	☐	☐
7. el cine	☐	☐	☐
8. limonada	☐	☐	☐

C. ¿Quién? Whose opinions are these? Draw a line from the photo of the person or persons to the opinions they express in the video.

1. Los cantores de Menudo bailan muy bien y cantan en inglés también.

2. Hay mucha gente en el restaurante.

3. La pizza en el restaurante italiano es muy rica.

4. Mirar a la gente es muy interesante.

5. Bailan más en México que en Estados Unidos.

6. Le es extraño siempre salir en coche.

D. Ventana cultural: ¿México o EE.UU.? As you listen to and watch
the video, indicate with an **X** which activities are typical of young people in
Mexico and which are typical of young people in the United States
(**EE.UU.**). In some instances, you may want to mark both columns.

México	EE.UU.	
☐	☐	1. Escuchan discos compactos.
☐	☐	2. Van al cine.
☐	☐	3. Comen al aire libre.
☐	☐	4. Comen pizza.
☐	☐	5. Toman limonada.
☐	☐	6. Van a fiestas.
☐	☐	7. Bailan.
☐	☐	8. Van a conciertos de rock.
☐	☐	9. Hablan por teléfono.
☐	☐	10. Pasean en coche.

11. Why is Daniel surprised that Kati goes out in a car instead of walking?

_____

12. Why do you think young people in Mexico and in the United States like
to do similar activities?

_____

13. Identify one activity that is typical of young people in Mexico but not
of young people in the United States. Why do you think this activity is
more popular in Mexico?

_____

In groups of four, compare and discuss your answers.

UNIDAD 4

CULTURAL MONTAGE:
San Antonio, Texas

To play the montage, use barcode
or counter:

| 21:06 | – | 21:51 |

Side 4, 9 to 1350

1. If you could visit San Antonio, Texas, what would you
like to do? Write some of the activities you saw in the video
that you would like to do.

_____

_____

_____

_____

2. Why, do you think, is there such a strong Mexican influence in San
Antonio?

_____

_____

_____

_____

3. The Alamo is a popular attraction for tourists, as well as for Texans. Why?

_____

_____

_____

_____

VIDEO WORKSHEETS *¡DIME! UNO*

LECCIÓN 1

PARA EMPEZAR

To play **Para empezar** from start to finish, use barcode or counter:

| 21:52 | – | 23:58 |

Side 4, 1373 to 5183

A. ¿Quién es? As you watch the video, draw a line from each person in the photo to his or her name.

Roberto   **Margarita**   **Pepe**   **Betty**   **Elena**   **Paquito**

Ana   **Patricio**   **Rafael**   **Kevin**   **Sarita**   **Lupe**

B. ¿Cuántos años? As you listen to Ana's description of her family, match the person with his or her age by marking an **X** in the appropriate column below.

	68	44	17	16	13	9	8	6
Ana								
Rafael								
Paquito								
Lupe								
Patricio								
Pepe								
Sarita								
Kevin								

C. La familia. Show the relationship between these people by drawing a line from each person in column A to the corresponding description of the relationship in column B.

A   **B**

a.   1. _____ es la novia de Rafael.

b.   2. _____ es la tía de Paquito.

c.   3. _____ es la hermana de Pepe.

d.   4. _____ es el padre de Rafael y Roberto.

e.   5. _____ es la abuela de Ana.

f.   6. _____ es el hijo de Betty.

g.   7. _____ es el primo de Paquito.

h.   8. _____ es el hermano de Rafael.

i.   9. _____ es el hermano de Ana.

D. ¿Cuántos años? As you listen to the video, complete the sentences below with the appropriate numbers written as words.

1. Rafael tiene _____ años.

2. Patricio tiene _____ años.

3. Kevin tiene _____ años.

4. El cumpleaños de Lupe es el _____ de marzo.

5. Mi cumpleaños es el _____ de junio.

6. El cumpleaños de papá es el _____ de enero.

Now check and correct your spelling.

sesenta y ocho	**diecisiete**	**doce**
diecinueve	**cuarenta y cuatro**	**treinta**

E. Ventana cultural: Los cumpleaños. How does Ana's family celebrate birthdays? How do you celebrate birthdays? Mark each of the following characteristics with **A (Ana)**, **M (my family)**, or both.

_____ family gathering   _____ dance music

_____ photos   _____ presents

_____ birthday cake   _____ video recorder

_____ cards   _____ party with friends

_____ piñata   _____ candles on a cake

Compare your responses with those of a classmate. What else did you observe about the birthday party for Patricio and Lupe? Tell your partner about any other special ways in which you celebrate your birthday.

¿QUÉ DECIMOS...?

To play **¿Qué decimos?** from start to finish, use barcode or counter:

| 23:59 | – | 28:16 |

Side 4, 5193 to 12904

A. Hola, tía. As you listen carefully to the video, circle the word or phrase that correctly completes each sentence.

1. Hoy es el (17, 19) de marzo.

2. Ya tengo (sesenta y dos, sesenta y ocho) años.

3. Aquí están papá, (tía Juliana, tía Elena) y tío Roberto.

4. Mira qué grandes están (mis hijos, mis nietos).

5. Estos dos gigantes son mis (mis hijos, mis sobrinos).

6. Primero los primos que son más (grandes, pequeños).

7. La boda va a ser en la iglesia de (San Antonio de Atocha, San Antonio de Padua).

B. ¿Qué dice? As you listen to the video, indicate who is being described by drawing a line from the statement to the corresponding person.

Lupe

Elena

1. Tiene sesenta y ocho años y todavía es joven y fuerte.

2. Pepe y Sarita son sus hijos.

3. Va a cumplir catorce años.

4. Tiene un anuncio.

5. Su hijo es Kevin.

6. Van a casarse el veinticuatro de junio.

Betty

Patricio

Rafael

C. Ventana cultural: El cumpleaños. Listen to the video again and sing the song with the family. When you have learned the song, sing it with a classmate.

1. How do you say "Happy Birthday" in Spanish?

_____

_____

2. How do you congratulate someone in Spanish when they announce a wedding date?

_____

_____

LECCIÓN 2

PARA EMPEZAR

A. ¿De veras? In the video, you learned about Ana's family and friends. For each of the people shown below, there are two questions. Answer the questions with **Sí** or **No**.

1. ¿Se llama Betty la nueva esposa de Rafael?   Sí   No
2. ¿Es ella profesora de inglés?   Sí   No

3. ¿Son Lupe y Betty las hermanastras de Kevin?   Sí   No
4. ¿Es Kevin el fotógrafo de la boda?   Sí   No

5. ¿Es Lola una cantante muy buena?   Sí   No
6. ¿Tiene Lola un novio que es futbolista?   Sí   No

7. ¿Es Juliana una escritora muy famosa?   Sí   No
8. ¿Es Juliana casada?   Sí   No

B. **¿Quién es?** As you listen to the video, draw a line from each description
below to the photo of the person being described.

Betty

Lola

1. Es futbolista.

2. Vive en México.

3. Es divorciada.

4. Es el hermanastro de Ana.

5. Es profesora de español.

6. Es la prima de Ana.

7. Es la madre de Betty.

8. Es el novio de Lola.

9. Tiene sesenta y nueve años.

Elvira

Mario

Kevin

Juliana

C. Es futbolista. Draw a line from each person below to his or her profession or future profession.

1. escritora

2. fotógrafo

3. futbolista

4. cantante

5. profesora

D. Ventana cultural: Las profesiones. Several professions are mentioned in the video. Do you think that these people would work in the same professions if they lived in Mexico? What if they all lived in San Antonio, Texas? In a group of four, discuss your answers.

¿QUÉ DECIMOS...?

To play **¿Qué decimos?** from start to finish, use barcode or counter:

| 30:13 | – | 33:46 |

Side 4, 16396 to 22799

A. Conversaciones. As you listen to the video, draw a line from each statement to the person who makes it.

1. **a.** ¿Conoces a estas personas?
    b. No a todas. Mi padrastro tiene muchos parientes.

2. **a.** Y tu abuelo, ¿dónde está?
    b. ¡No tengo abuelo! Mi abuela es viuda.

3. **a.** Y tú, ¿qué quieres ser?
    b. Yo quiero ser reportero como mi papá.

4. **a.** ¿Quiénes son esas dos chicas?
    b. Son mis primas, Leslie y Pamela.

B.¿Quién? Below are descriptions of some of the people at the wedding. Identify each person by marking an **X** in the appropriate box.

	Kevin	Paquito	Elvira	Juliana	Rafael	Pamela
1. Tiene muchos parientes.						
2. No le gustan las bodas.						
3. Es viuda.						
4. Es escritora.						
5. Quiere ser reportero.						
6. Es reportero.						
7. Es el hermanastro de Paquito.						
8. Es la prima de Kevin.						

C. Ventana cultural: La recepción. As you watch the video, mark an
X next to the things you see at Rafael and Betty's wedding reception.

☐ punch   ☐ photographer

☐ games   ☐ eating

☐ relatives   ☐ pets

☐ musicians   ☐ wedding cake

☐ food   ☐ piñata

☐ dancing   ☐ flowers

What else did you see?

_____

_____

_____

Discuss your responses with a classmate. If either of you has been to a
wedding reception, compare it to this reception. Are there any differences?

LECCIÓN 3

PARA EMPEZAR

To play **Para empezar** from start to finish, use barcode or counter:

| 33:47 | – | 36:05 |

Side 4, 22806 to 26952

A. ¿Cierto o falso? As you listen to Paquito's description of his father's wedding reception, indicate whether each statement is **C (cierto)** or **F (falso)** by circling the correct response.

C   F   **1.** Betty está muy nerviosa.

C   F   **2.** La abuela y la madre de Betty están llorando porque están tristes.

C   F   **3.** La banda está tocando música mexicana.

C   F   **4.** Pepe quiere comer pastel.

C   F   **5.** La abuela le permite comer el pastel.

C   F   **6.** Pamela y Leslie quieren bailar con Julio.

C   F   **7.** Paquito está aburrido.

B. ¿Qué dice? As you listen carefully to the video, complete each sentence by circling the appropriate word.

1. Betty está (lista, triste) para entrar en la iglesia.

2. Pero no están tristes; están (ridículas, emocionadas).

3. ¡Qué (divertidas, ridículas) son las bodas!

4. ¡Pero nadie está (bailando, cantando)…sólo Papá y Betty.

5. Pepe está (furioso, contento).

6. ¡Qué mala (música, suerte)!

7. Julio está (bebiendo, comiendo) ponche.

8. Kevin está (cantando, hablando) con una chica.

Nombre _____ Fecha _____

C. Ventana cultural: ¿Opinión o sentimiento? In the list below, which words are used to express opinions, and which are used to express feelings? Below are words that you heard Paquito use. Mark each word accordingly: **O (opinión)** or **S (sentimiento)**.

1. _____ furioso

2. _____ emocionado

3. _____ aburrido

4. _____ romántico

5. _____ cansado

6. _____ ridículo

7. _____ nervioso

8. _____ triste

9. _____ contento

10. _____ suerte

With a classmate discuss your responses. Did you agree? Are there any words that might indicate both an opinion and a feeling?

¿QUÉ DECIMOS. . .?

A. ¿Quién? Read the sentences below and listen carefully to the video. Then select the correct completion for each sentence by circling the letter of the appropriate word or phrase.

To play **¿Qué decimos?** from start to finish, use barcode or counter:

| 36:06 | – | 38:57 |

Side 4, 26960 to 32110

1. A _____ le encantan las bodas.

   a. Pamela   **b.** Leslie   **c.** Ana

2. Kevin es el _____ de Pamela y Leslie.

   a. hermanastro   **b.** primo   **c.** hermano

3. Kevin está con su amigo _____.

   a. Mario   **b.** Paquito   **c.** Julio

4. Julio es _____ en la opinión de Leslie.

   a. guapo   **b.** feo   **c.** rico

5. Los chicos están _____.

   a. bailando   **b.** hablando   **c.** cantando

6. Los novios están _____.

   a. hablando   **b.** bailando   **c.** comiendo

7. Kevin está bailando con _____.

   a. Lupe   **b.** Pamela   **c.** Leslie

8. _____ tiene mala suerte.

   a. Kevin   **b.** Pamela   **c.** Leslie

9. _____ está nerviosa.

   a. Pamela   **b.** Leslie   **c.** Ana

10. Los novios van a _____.

   a. tocar la música   **b.** cortar el pastel   **c.** servir la comida

B. Es tan guapo.
Read the following descriptions. As you listen to the video, draw a line from each description to the photo of the person(s) being described.

Julio

Pamela

Leslie

1. Le encantan las bodas.

2. Vienen hacia Pamela y Leslie.

3. Están bailando.

4. Tiene mala suerte.

5. Es el nuevo primo de Pamela y Leslie.

6. Está conversando con Ana.

7. Está triste.

8. Van a cortar el pastel.

9. Está cansada.

10. Es muy guapo.

Kevin

Betty y Rafael

C. Ventana cultural: Expresiones.
In the video, you heard various expressions. Mark an **X** next to each of the expressions you heard in the video.

1. ☐ ¡Qué mala suerte!

2. ☐ ¿Verdad?

3. ☐ ¡Qué tonta eres!

4. ☐ Dime.

5. ☐ Claro que sí.

6. ☐ No sé.

7. ☐ ¡Qué ridículo!

8. ☐ ¿De veras?

9. ☐ ¿Qué pasa?

10. ☐ ¡Cuánta gente!

In groups of three, think of situations in which you would use each expression. Can you make up short conversations using these expressions? Perform one of the conversations for another group.

Nombre _____ Feche _____

 UNIDAD 5

CULTURAL MONTAGE:
Madrid, España

Indicate whether the following are similarities or differences between your city and Madrid. Mark **S** for similarity or **D** for difference.

To play the montage, use barcode or counter:

| 00:00 | – | 00:40 |

Side 5, 10 to 1214

Madrid	Your City
1. large post office building	_____
2. big buildings	_____
3. fountains and statues in intersections	_____
4. balconies on houses	_____
5. walk/don't walk lights represented as people	_____
6. traffic	_____
7. large park with a lake	_____
8. Royal Palace	_____
9. gates to the city	_____

LECCIÓN 1

PARA EMPEZAR

To play **Para empezar** from start to finish, use barcode or counter:

| 00:41 | – | 02:56 |

Side 5, 2149 to 5305

A. ¿A la izquierda? Look carefully at the map of the city. As you listen to the video, mark the route that each person takes by drawing a line from where he or she is standing, along the path he or she follows, to his or her destination.

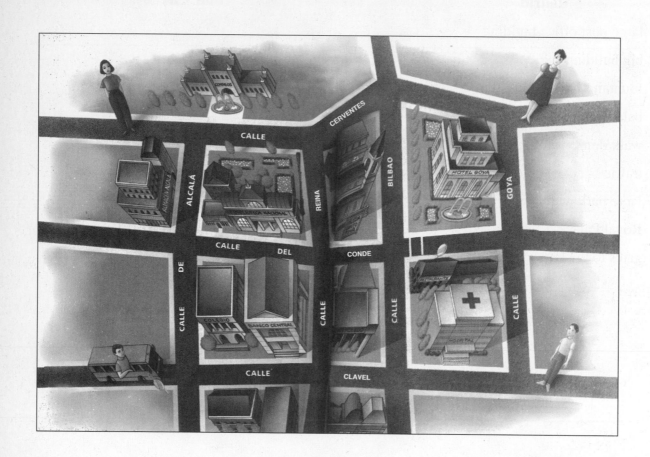

B. Dobla a la derecha. Mientras escuchas el video, escribe el nombre de la persona quien recibe estas direcciones.

Carla   **Enrique**   **Mariseta**   **Luis**

1. _____ necesita regresar al hotel: Tienes que tomar el autobús número 6. Bájate enfrente del restaurante. Cruza la calle y camina hasta la esquina de la calle Goya.

2. _____ necesita cambiar un cheque de viajero: Hay que caminar una cuadra y doblar a la izquierda. Luego camina dos cuadras más y dobla a la derecha. El banco está en la esquina de Reina y Clavel.

3. _____ tiene que ir al almacén. Queda muy cerca: Debes doblar a la derecha y caminar una cuadra. Enfrente del almacén hay una tienda y un café.

4. _____ necesita enviar unas tarjetas postales: Tienes que seguir por la calle Clavel hasta la calle de Alcalá. Dobla a la derecha y camina dos cuadras. Cruza la calle y correos está detrás de la fuente.

C. Ventana cultural: Las calles. Frecuentemente, los nombres de las calles son nombres de personas famosas o de lugares famosos.

1. ¿Cuáles de estos nombres se mencionan en el video? Marca con una **X** los nombres mencionados.

☐ Calle Goya   ☐ Calle Cedro

☐ Calle Bilbao   ☐ Calle Reina

☐ Calle Velázquez   ☐ Calle Clavel

☐ Calle Cervantes   ☐ Calle Alcalá

☐ Calle Encina   ☐ Calle del Conde

2. ¿Hay calles o avenidas en tu ciudad o pueblo con nombres españoles? Escribe los nombres de tres o cuatro calles con nombres españoles. Marca los que son nombres de personas con **P (persona)** y los que son nombres de lugares con **L (lugares)**.

_____

_____

_____

_____

¿QUÉ DECIMOS...?

To play ¿Qué decimos? from start to finish, use barcode or counter:

02:57 – 06:31

Side 5, 5318 to 11720

A. Al pedir instrucciones. Manolo tiene que seguir instrucciones específicas para llegar a correos. Enumera las instrucciones que recibe en orden cronológico.

_____ **a.** Toma el metro para Ventas y bájate en la estación Banco de España.

_____ **b.** Sigue dos manzanas y dobla a la derecha.

_____ **c.** Baja a la recepción y pregunta cómo se llega.

_____ **d.** Al salir del hotel, dobla a la derecha.

_____ **e.** Camina dos manzanas y dobla a la izquierda.

B. ¿Quién dice esto? Mientras escuchas el video, identifica a la persona que hace cada comentario y conecta su nombre con el comentario.

1. ¡Pero, mamá! ¿Tengo que llevar a Víctor?

    a. mamá

2. Baja a la recepción y pregunta cómo se llega.

    b. Manolo

    c. papá

3. Y Víctor, no olviden. Deben estar en el restaurante del hotel antes de las cinco.

    d. Víctor

    e. la recepcionista

4. Al salir del hotel dobla a la derecha.

5. Toma el metro y bájate en la estación Banco de España.

6. ¿Eso es correos?

7. ¡Vamos de compras!

C. Una familia argentina. Mientras escuchas el video, escribe la palabra apropiada para completer la frase.

1. Deben ir a la oficina de correos a comprar _____.

2. Deben estar en el _____ antes de las cinco.

3. Camina dos manzanas más y dobla a la _____.

4. Está allí mismo, detrás de _____.

5. A ver. Dame. Mil _____ pesetas.

D. Ventana cultural: Manolo es de Argentina. In the video the receptionist gives Manolo directions to the post office. Manolo has some difficulty understanding her.

What word gives him a problem?

_____

What word would he have understood?

_____

In groups of three, discuss why you think this confusion occurred. Do any of you know words used in the United States that would confuse someone from England, or vice versa?

LECCIÓN 2

PARA EMPEZAR

To play **Para empezar** from start to finish, use barcode or counter:

06:32 – 09:16

Side 5, 11757 to 16676

A. ¿Qué prefiere? Mira y escucha el video y marca con una **X** toda la ropa que compran los espías.

☐ un impermeable beige   ☐ un sombrero negro

☐ un vestido verde   ☐ una camiseta anaranjada

☐ una falda rosada   ☐ unos calcetines grises

☐ unos jeans   ☐ una camiseta azul

☐ una camiseta amarilla   ☐ una blusa negra

☐ unos zapatos deportivos   ☐ una blusa verde

☐ una sudadera gris   ☐ unos calcetines azules

☐ un traje azul   ☐ una blusa roja

☐ unos pantalones grises   ☐ un vestido rosado

B. ¿Qué dice? ¿Qué ropa miran los espías? Marca con un círculo la palabra que completa cada oración, según el video.

1. Llevan impermeables beige y (sombreros / vestidos) negros.

2. Por ejemplo, ese (suéter / vestido) es muy elegante.

3. Y ese (traje / impermeable) le gusta mucho al espía.

4. Están mirando las (camisetas / blusas).

5. El dependiente le recomienda unos (sombreros / pantalones) grises.

6. El espía compra un par de (calcetines / zapatos) azules.

7. Pero la (sudadera / blusa) no combina muy bien con la falda.

8. Entonces se prueba unos jeans y una (sudadera / camiseta) gris.

C. Ventana cultural: ¡De compras! El Corte Inglés is a large
department store in Spain, similar to large department stores in the United
States. How does it compare to a department store in your city or town?

Similarities

_____

_____

_____

_____

Differences

_____

_____

_____

_____

Compare your answers with those of a classmate.

¿QUÉ DECIMOS...?

To play **¿Qué decimos?** from start to finish, use barcode or counter:

| 09:17 | – | 12:39 |

Side 5, 16710 to 22750

A. ¿Cierto o falso? Manolo y Víctor están en el Corte Inglés. Mientras escuchas el video, indica si cada oración es **C (cierto)** o **F (falso)**.

C   F   **1.** El almacén es fantástico.

C   F   **2.** Manolo y Víctor van por el ascensor.

C   F   **3.** Las camisetas les gustan mucho a las chicas.

C   F   **4.** Manolo quiere una camiseta roja para su novia.

C   F   **5.** La camiseta cuesta dos mil setecientas pesetas.

C   F   **6.** Las tallas en España son iguales que en Argentina.

C   F   **7.** Manolo paga en la caja.

C   F   **8.** La camisa cuesta 4.900 pesetas.

C   F   **9.** Manolo y Víctor tienen más dinero.

B. ¿Qué les gusta? Manolo y Víctor ven mucha ropa cuando van de compras. Marca con una **X** la ropa que ven en el almacén.

☐ una camiseta roja   ☐ unos zapatos

☐ una blusa azul   ☐ una camisa roja

☐ una camiseta amarilla   ☐ una chaqueta negra

☐ una camiseta azul   ☐ un vestido rosado

C. ¿Qué dice? As you listen to the video, indicate whether Manolo or Víctor makes each statement or question by drawing a line from the sentence to the person who is speaking.

Manolo

1. ¿Cómo que no tenemos dinero?

2. Perfecta. Me encanta. ¿Dónde pago?

3. Vamos por las escaleras.

4. Las tallas aquí son diferentes.

5. Estoy buscando un regalo para mi novia.

6. Hay unos zapatos fabulosos.

7. Recuerda que parte del dinero es mío también.

Víctor

D. Ventana cultural: El almacén. In the department store, there are different departments for different kinds of clothing or merchandise. Can you tell what you would find in the following departments?

1. camisería: _____

2. zapatería: _____

3. sombrerería: _____

4. perfumería: _____

Can you guess what a store that sells **frutas** would be called? A store that sells **leche**?

5. frutas: _____

6. leche: _____

LECCIÓN 3

To play **Para empezar** from start to finish, use barcode or counter:

| 12:40 | – | 17:01 |

Side 5, 22778 to 30600

PARA EMPEZAR

A. ¿Qué pedimos? Marca con una **X** las comidas que se piden en el video.

☐ café con leche	☐ agua mineral con gas
☐ agua mineral sin gas	☐ bocadillo de jamón serrano
☐ bocadillo de jamón york	☐ limonada
☐ café	☐ manzanas
☐ melón	☐ naranjas
☐ pizza	☐ bizcocho
☐ hamburguesa	☐ perrito
☐ refresco	☐ sándwich de queso
☐ sándwich mixto	☐ sándwich de jamón

B. **¿Qué dice?** Escucha la conversación entre el camarero y los clientes en el restaurante. Indica la letra de la palabra o frase que completa cada oración, según el video.

1. Van a ver que la vida de un _____ no es fácil.
   a. cliente
   b. camarero
   c. cocinero

2. No quiero tomar nada _____.
   a. caliente
   b. frío
   c. sin gas

3. No tengo hambre. Tengo _____.
   a. calor
   b. frío
   c. sed

4. El _____ es la especialidad de la casa.
   a. bocadillo
   b. melón
   c. bizcocho

5. Me trae una _____ para comer el melón, por favor.
   a. manzana
   b. cuchara
   c. cuenta

6. Luisito, siempre pides un _____ y un refresco.
   a. perrito
   b. hamburguesa
   c. bocadillo

7. Sí, claro. Un sándwich _____.
   a. de queso
   b. mixto
   c. de jamón

8. Aquí dice que el _____ va incluido.
   a. servicio
   b. café
   c. refresco

C. Ventana cultural: La comida.

1. En España a mucha gente le gusta comer fruta de postre. ¿Cuáles son las frutas mencionadas en el video?

   _____

   _____

   _____

2. En el video un hombre pide un bocadillo y una mujer pide un sándwich. ¿Cuál es la diferencia entre un bocadillo y un sándwich?

   _____

   _____

   _____

Compara tu respuesta con la de un compañero de clase.

¿QUÉ DECIMOS...?

To play ¿Qué decimos? from start to finish, use barcode or counter:

| 17:02 | – | 19:58 |

Side 5, 30623 to 35909

A. ¿Quiénes? As you listen carefully to the video, mark an **X** in the column under the photo of the person who is being described..

	Camarero	Papá	Mamá	Manolo	Víctor
1. Está muy cansado.	☐	☐	☐	☐	☐
2. Tiene mucha hambre.	☐	☐	☐	☐	☐
3. Llegan tarde.	☐	☐	☐	☐	☐
4. Dice que hay una mesa libre.	☐	☐	☐	☐	☐
5. Pregunta si quieren ver la carta.	☐	☐	☐	☐	☐
6. Siempre pide lo mismo.	☐	☐	☐	☐	☐
7. Tiene mucha sed.	☐	☐	☐	☐	☐
8. Van a merendar.	☐	☐	☐	☐	☐
9. Quiere bizcocho.	☐	☐	☐	☐	☐
10. Dice que el sándwich mixto lleva jamón y queso.	☐	☐	☐	☐	☐
11. Pide agua mineral.	☐	☐	☐	☐	☐
12. Pide melón.	☐	☐	☐	☐	☐
13. Dicen "papas fritas".	☐	☐	☐	☐	☐
14. No quiere limonada.	☐	☐	☐	☐	☐
15. Quiere probar las papas fritas.	☐	☐	☐	☐	☐
16. Dice "Deja de jugar con la cuchara".	☐	☐	☐	☐	☐
17. Se queja del dinero y de las papas fritas.	☐	☐	☐	☐	☐
18. Quiere la cuenta.	☐	☐	☐	☐	☐
19. Tiene razón.	☐	☐	☐	☐	☐
20. Fue amable.	☐	☐	☐	☐	☐

© McDougal Littell, Inc.

B. ¿Qué piden? As you listen to the video, mark an **X** beside the foods and drinks that each member of the family orders.

Papá	Mamá	Víctor	Manolo
☐ sándwich mixto	☐ hamburguesa	☐ hamburguesa	☐ bizcocho
☐ papas fritas	☐ bizcocho	☐ agua mineral	☐ papas fritas
☐ agua mineral	☐ café con leche	☐ café con leche	☐ melón
☐ limonada	☐ limonada	☐ papas fritas	☐ limonada

C. Respuestas. Read the sentences and responses below. As you listen to the video, match the statements or questions in column A with the corresponding responses in column B.

A

_____ 1. ¿Por qué llegan tan tarde?
¿Qué hicieron?

_____ 2. Hamburguesas y más hamburguesas.

_____ 3. Recuerda que ahora
sólo vamos a merendar.

_____ 4. ¿De qué es el sándwich mixto?

_____ 5. Y para él, una hamburguesa
con papas fritas.

_____ 6. ¿Y por qué comes tan rápido?

_____ 7. ¿Desean algo más?

_____ 8. ¿Cuánto le doy de propina?

B

a. Sí, con patatas fritas.

b. El servicio va incluido.

c. ¡Estos niños!

d. ¡Siempre pides lo mismo!

e. Sólo la cuenta, por favor.

f. Fuimos al Corte Inglés.

g. Para mi melón.

h. ¡No tenemos prisa!

i. Lleva jamón y queso.

j. Más tarde cenamos.

Nombre _____ Fecha _____

U N I D A D 6

CULTURAL MONTAGE:
Guadalajara, México

To play the montage, use barcode or counter:

| 20:08 | – | 20:46 |

Side 6, 11 to 1170

1. a. What do you think the **centro histórico** would include in Guadalajara?

   _____

   _____

   _____

   b. What would the **centro histórico** include in your city or town?

   _____

   _____

   _____

2. The Guadalajara area is famous for handicrafts. List the handicrafts you
    saw in this montage.

   _____

   _____

   _____

3. Murals by José Clemente Orozco can be seen throughout Guadalajara.
    What is your impression of the mural shown in the montage?

   _____

   _____

   _____

LECCIÓN 1

To play **Para empezar** from start to finish, use barcode or counter:

| 20:47 | – | 25:51 |

Side 6, 1189 to 10312

PARA EMPEZAR

A. ¿Quién lo hace? Mientras escuchas el video, indica quién hace las cosas indicadas. Haz un círculo alrededor de la foto de cada persona.

1. Descubre que no hay papas.

2. Encontró a Javier.

3. Le encantó el mural en el Palacio de Gobierno.

4. Pagó las bebidas.

5. Empezó a llorar.

6. Sólo tiene quince mil pesos.

© McDougal Littell, Inc.

B. ¿Qué pasó? Para ver como fue el día de Óscar, enumera estos eventos en el orden en que ocurren en el video.

a. _____ Los mariachis tocaron y cantaron tan bien que Mónica empezó a llorar.

b. _____ La señora Domínguez empezó a preparar la comida.

c. _____ Visitaron el Teatro Degollado.

d. _____ Los chicos acompañaron a las chicas a su casa en taxi.

e. _____ Las chicas pasaron mucho tiempo mirando las artesanías.

f. _____ La señora le dio un billete de cincuenta mil pesos a Óscar.

g. _____ Óscar sólo tiene quince mil pesos.

h. _____ Óscar y Javier encontraron a Lilia y Mónica.

C. Ventana cultural: ¿Adónde fueron? Identify the places Óscar and his friends visited by connecting the name with the corredponding photo of the place.

1.

2.

el Palacio de Gobierno

el Mercado Libertad

el Palacio de Gobierno

el Mercado Libertad

3.

4.

With a partner discuss which of these places you would like to visit and why.

¿QUÉ DECIMOS...?

A. ¡Estupendo! A Mónica le gusta mucho Guadalajara. Marca con una **X** las palabras que Mónica usa para describir la ciudad y sus actividades.

To play **¿Qué decimos?** from start to finish, use barcode or counter:

25:52 – 31:19

Side 6, 10336 to 20140

☐ romántica   ☐ bellas   ☐ riquísima

☐ contenta   ☐ simpáticos   ☐ extraños

☐ linda   ☐ pequeño   ☐ aburrido

☐ divertido   ☐ impresionante   ☐ enorme

☐ bonitas   ☐ fea   ☐ hermosísima

☐ interesante   ☐ preciosas   ☐ guapo

B. ¿Qué dice? ¿Qué escribió Mónica en su carta? Completa cada oración con la palabra o la frase apropiada que oíste en el video.

1. Me _____ con una docena de rosas.

2. Por la mañana Lilia me _____ al centro.

3. Los primos de Lilia _____ acompañarnos al Teatro Degollado.

4. Me _____ una blusa hermosísima.

5. Los primos de Lilia _____ la música.

¿Están todas las palabras deletreadas bien?

compré   decidieron   llevó   pagaron   recibieron

C. ¿Quiénes? ¿Quiénes hicieron estas actividades? Haz una línea de cada actividad a la foto de la persona que la hizo. En algunos casos más de una persona hizo la actividad.

Óscar

Javier

1. Recibió a Mónica con una docena de rosas.

2. Pasearon en una calandria.

3. Acompañaron a las chicas al Teatro Degollado.

4. No resistió más y compró una blusa hermosísima.

5. Pagaron la música de los mariachis.

Mónica

Lilia

D. Ventana cultural: El mercado. El Mercado Libertad is a fascinating place and the focal point for shopping in Guadalajara. As you watched the video, you saw many of the items that are sold in the market. With a classmate, make a list of the items that you saw.

_____   _____

_____   _____

_____   _____

_____   _____

_____   _____

Now compare your list with that of another pair of classmates.

Is there a market near where you live where you could buy the items that you listed?

LECCIÓN 2

PARA EMPEZAR

A. ¿Quién es? Mientras escuchas el video, indica quién hace esto. Haz una línea entre lo que cada persona hace y la foto de la persona.

Mónica

Óscar

Toño

1. Vio a su novia Mónica con otro chico.

2. Él compró una figurita de vidrio.

3. Está tan triste.

4. Compró un plato de cerámica.

5. ¡Le dio la cacatúa al chico!

6. No tengo nada que hacer.

7. ¡Qué tonto eres!

8. Acaba de llegar a Guadalajara.

B. Respuestas. Mientras escuchas el video, marca con un círculo la letra de la reacción que oyes en el video a estas oraciones.

1. Ayer Óscar fue al cine, ¿y sabes a quién vio?

   a. No sé.

   b. ¡Vio a su novia Mónica con otro chico!

2. El chico compró una figurita de vidrio y le dio la figurita a Mónica.

   a. También compró una cacatúa de papel maché.

   b. Fue un gesto romántico, ¿no crees?

3. Compró una cacatúa de papel maché. Y ¡le dio la cacatúa al chico!

   a. ¡Ella nunca me dio nada a mí!

   b. Fue un gesto romántico, ¿no crees?

4. ¿Quieres salir con nosotros?

   a. Estoy demasiado triste. Prefiero estar solo.

   b. Ven, vamos a tomar algo.

5. Mira, te quiero presentar a mi hermano, Toño.

   a. Yo también vi a Mónica con él.

   b. Acaba de llegar a Guadalajara.

C. Ventana cultural: Las artesanías. Mónica tiene mucho interés en las artesanías de México. ¿Puedes identificar estas cosas? Dibuja una línea del nombre al artículo.

a.

1. un plato de cerámica

2. una figurita de vidrio

3. una cacatúa de papel maché

b.

c.

¿QUÉ DECIMOS...?

To play ¿Qué decimos? from start to finish, use barcode or counter:

| 34:02 | – | 37:16 |

Side 6, 25015 to 30820

A. ¿Cierto o falso? Mientras escuchas el video, indica con un círculo si cada oración es **C (cierto)** o **F (falso)**.

C   F   **1.** Mónica conoce Tlaquepaque.

C   F   **2.** Lilia y Mónica van a Chapala el sábado.

C   F   **3.** Mónica le escribe una carta a Lilia.

C   F   **4.** Tlaquepaque es un pueblo pintoresco.

C   F   **5.** En Tlaquepaque venden todo tipo de artesanías.

C   F   **6.** A Mónica no le gusta ir de compras.

C   F   **7.** A Mónica no le gusta nada la cerámica.

C   F   **8.** Mónica compró un recuerdo muy bonito para Óscar.

C   F   **9.** Fue imposible subir al coche los cuatro.

C   F   **10.** Óscar y Mónica decidieron tomar el autobús.

B. ¿Qué dice? Lee las oraciones. Luego escucha el video e indica la letra de la palabra o la frase que completa cada oración en el video.

1. Mónica no conoce _____.

    a. Guadalajara   **b.** Chapala   **c.** Tlaquepaque

2. ¿Por qué no vamos_____?

    a. el sábado   **b.** el domingo   **c.** el lunes

3. Ayer Lilia y yo fuimos con _____ a Tlaquepaque.

    a. Óscar y Javier   **b.** Isabel   **c.** las primas

4. ¡Ya sabes cuánto me gusta _____!

    a. pasar horas allí   **b.** ir de compras   **c.** escribir cartas

5. Más que nada me gustó _____.

    a. las figuritas de vidrio   **b.** la cerámica   **c.** las cosas de papel maché

6. _____ y yo decidimos regresar en autobús— o camión.

    a. Óscar   **b.** Javier   **c.** Lilia

C. Ventana cultural: Las artesanías. The handicrafts of Tlaquepaque are fashioned with skill and artistry. Of the items that you saw in the video, which would you like to buy for yourself? Why?

_____

_____

_____

_____

_____

In groups of four, compare your answers. Did any of you agree?

Which item do you think would be a good present for your Spanish teacher?

PARA EMPEZAR

To play **Para empezar** from start to
finish, use barcode or counter:

37:17 – **40:57**

Side 6, 30853 to 37439

A. ¿Quién es? Lee las siguientes oraciones e indica con un
círculo si describen a **Iztaccíhuatl (I)**, al **rey (R)**, o a
Popocatépetl (P).

I	R	P	**1.**	Es la joya más preciosa del mundo.
I	R	P	**2.**	Tuvo que buscar un soldado fuerte y valiente.
I	R	P	**3.**	Se enamoró del soldado inmediatamente.
I	R	P	**4.**	Luchó valientemente.
I	R	P	**5.**	Se puso tan triste que se enfermó y murió.
I	R	P	**6.**	Regresó victorioso a la ciudad.
I	R	P	**7.**	Construyó una pirámide.
I	R	P	**8.**	Duermen a poca distancia de la capital.

B. Ventana cultural: Las leyendas. The early people of Mexico, like the early people of most civilizations, explained natural phenomena in their legends. The legend of **Popocatépetl** and **Iztaccíhuatl** is an example of such a legend. Do you know any other legends that explain natural phenomena? What is the origin of the legends? With a partner answer these questions.

What does the legend explain?

Two volcanoes near Mexico City

_____

_____

_____

_____

What is the country of origin of the legend?

Mexico

_____

_____

_____

_____

¿QUÉ DECIMOS...?

To play **¿Qué decimos?** from start to finish, use barcode or counter:

| 40:58 | – | 43:36 |

Side 6, 37474 to 42213

A. ¿Cierto o falso? Mientras escuchas el video, indica con un círculo si esta información es **C (cierta)** o **F (falsa)** según el video.

1. Mónica llegó temprano.   C   F

2. No pudieron subir todos al coche.   C   F

3. Óscar y Mónica tuvieron que regresar en coche.   C   F

4. Mónica entró a una tienda a comprar un sándwich.   C   F

5. Al salir de la tienda, Mónica buscó a Óscar y lo encontró. C   F

6. Óscar empezó a correr hacia el camión.   C   F

7. Gritó pero el chofer no lo oyó y siguió adelante.   C   F

8. Óscar golpeó la puerta del camión.   C   F

9. Por fin, el chofer lo vio y paró el coche.   C   F

B. **¿Qué dice?** Mónica está hablando con la madre de Lilia. Completa cada oración con la palabra apropiada según el video.

1. **La madre:** ¡Por fin _____ !

2. **Mónica:** Es que _____ un problema en Tlaquepaque.

3. **Mónica:** Tuvimos que esperar un buen rato y mientras tanto,

   _____ en otro regalo para mi mamá.

4. **Mónica:** _____ a Óscar pero no lo encontré.

5. **Mónica:** Pues él me vio subir y _____ a correr hacia el camión.

6. **La madre:** ¡Ay, no! ¿Lo _____ allá en Tlaquepaque?

7. **Mónica:** Óscar es mi héroe. Es como Popocatépetl, de la leyenda que

   _____ en el avión.

C. **¿Sí o no?** Mientras escuchas el video, contesta estas preguntas. Marca con un círculo **Sí** o **No**.

1.	¿Tuvieron un problema Mónica y sus amigos?	Sí	No
2.	¿Pudieron subir todos al coche?	Sí	No
3.	¿Pensó Mónica en otro regalo?	Sí	No
4.	¿Entró Mónica a la tienda por mucho tiempo?	Sí	No
5.	¿Encontró Mónica a Óscar?	Sí	No
6.	¿Vio Óscar a Mónica subir al camión?	Sí	No
7.	¿Decidió Óscar correr hacia el camión?	Sí	No
8.	¿Lo oyó el chofer?	Sí	No

D. Ventana cultural: ¡Qué héroe! Mónica tells Lilia's mother that
Óscar is like Popocatépetl. In groups of three, discuss the traits that both
Óscar and Popocatépetl show. Are these the traits of a hero?

Popocatépetl   **Óscar**

_____   _____

_____   _____

_____   _____

_____   _____

_____   _____

UNIDAD 7

CULTURAL MONTAGE:
Miami, Florida

To play the montage, use barcode or counter:

| 00:00 | – | 00:50 |

Side 7, 13 to 1523

1. **a.** Why are so many water and beach sports shown in this Miami montage?

_____

_____

_____

b. How many of the sports that you saw in the video can you name in Spanish?

_____

_____

_____

c. What other water sports might you see in Miami?

_____

_____

_____

2. **a.** Why are some signs written in Spanish in Miami?

_____

_____

_____

b. What signs did you see?

_____

_____

_____

LECCIÓN 1

PARA EMPEZAR

To play **Para empezar** from start to finish, use barcode or counter:

00:51 – 04:22

Side 7, 1543 to 7868

A. Deportes. Mientras escuchas la descripción de la quinta Olimpíada Atlética y Académica, enumera las fotos en el orden en que se mencionan en el video.

a. _____

b. _____

c. _____

d. _____

e. _____

f. _____

B. En Miami. La Olimpíada de Miami es interesante e importante para los estudiantes. Mientras escuchas el video, dibuja un círculo alrededor de la palabra o la frase que mejor completa cada oración.

1. La Olimpiada en Miami es (atlética y académica, solamente atlética).

2. Hubo un gran partido en el campo de (béisbol, fútbol).

3. Hubo un partido de baloncesto entre los equipos (masculinos, femeninos) de South Miami y de Sunset.

4. Rafaela Delgado salió (primero, segundo).

5. Samuel Rodríguez ganó la competencia de (jai alai, salto de altura).

6. Hubo una exhibición de (jai alai, juegos académicos) por primera vez.

7. Killian High School ganó la competencia de (historia, ciclismo).

C. ¿Qué deporte? Varios estudiantes sobresalieron en la Olimpíada de Miami. Mientras escuchas el video, escribe en qué deporte sobresalieron estos estudiantes.

Jorge Campos _____

Rafaela Delgado _____

Juan Colón _____

Samuel Rodríguez _____

Paula Wilson _____

D. Ventana cultural: Deportes. Sports are as popular in Spanish-speaking countries as they are in the United States. One of the sports mentioned in the video is a sport that originated in the Basque region of Spain and is played in many Spanish-speaking countries. One of the few places in the United States that it is played is Miami. What sport is this?

_____

Based on what you saw in the video, write three words—in Spanish—that describe this game.

_____

_____

_____

¿QUÉ DECIMOS...?

To play ¿Qué decimos? from start
to finish, use barcode or counter:

| 04:23 | – | 07:32 |

Side 7, 7888 to 13542

A. ¿Qué dice? Mientras escuchas las conversaciones en el video, haz una línea de cada oración a la persona que la dice.

1.

Alfredo

José Luis

a. (Las Panteras no tienen buen equipo.)

b. (Tienes razón. Nosotros somos mejores.)

2.

Papá

Mamá

a. (Es el número seis. Juega muy bien.)

b. (Mira el partido. José Luis acaba de entrar.)

3.

José Luis

Mamá

Papá

a. (¡José Luis, corazón! ¿Estás lastimado?)

b. (Estoy bien.)

c. (¿Qué pasó?)

d. (El árbitro les cobró una falta.)

B. **¿A quién?** Mientras miras y escuchas el video, indica con un círculo la persona a quién o de quién se habla.

1. Oye,  , ¿estás listo?

2. es el número seis.

3.  , mira el partido.

4.  también juega béisbol.

5. ¡ va a meter un gol!

6. ¡ , haz algo!

7. ¡ , corazón! ¿Estás lastimado?

8. ¡Ay, ! Te digo que estoy bien.

C. **Ventana cultural: El fútbol.** El fútbol es un deporte muy popular en los países hispanohablantes. Como el fútbol americano, el fútbol tiene un vocabulario muy especial. Escribe todas las palabras de este deporte que oíste en el video. Hay más o menos diez.

_____   _____

_____   _____

_____   _____

_____   _____

_____

LECCIÓN 2

To play **Para empezar** from start to finish, use barcode or counter:

07:33 – 10:25

Side 7, 13595 to 18743

PARA EMPEZAR

A. ¿Qué le duele? María Teresa está enferma. Mientras escuchas el video, marca con una **X** las partes del cuerpo que dice que le duelen.

El cuerpo humano

- cabeza ☐
- pelo ☐
- garganta ☐
- pecho ☐
- dedos ☐
- estómago ☐
- cuello ☐
- brazo ☐
- espalda ☐
- mano (f) ☐
- pierna ☐
- rodilla ☐
- tobillo ☐
- pie ☐

B. ¿Sí o No? María Teresa no está muy bien. Contesta estas preguntas con **Sí** o **No**.

1. ¿Quiere ir a la escuela María Teresa?   Sí   No
2. ¿Hizo su tarea anoche?   Sí   No
3. ¿Le duele la cabeza?   Sí   No
4. ¿Quiere tomar aspirinas?   Sí   No
5. ¿Le duele a María Teresa la pierna?   Sí   No
6. ¿Se cayó durante el partido de fútbol?   Sí   No
7. ¿Fue un golpe serio?   Sí   No
8. ¿Es hoy sábado?   Sí   No

C. Ventana cultural: ¿María Teresa o tú? Below are descriptions of María Teresa's activities. Mark an **X** before each activity that describes you, too.

☐ No hizo la tarea.

☐ No quiere tomar aspirina.

☐ Va a misa.

☐ No durmió bien.

☐ Se cayó durante el partido de fútbol.

☐ Hace un picnic en el parque.

Are any of these activities typical of you and your friends? Do you think they are also typical of young people in Mexico? Discuss these questions with a classmate.

¿QUÉ DECIMOS...?

A. ¿Qué dice? Lee las siguientes oraciones. Luego escucha cuidadosamente para ver quién las dice en el video. Haz una línea de cada oración a la foto de la persona que la dice.

To play **¿Qué decimos?** from start to finish, use barcode or counter:

10:26 – 13:52

Side 7, 18771 to 24962

1. ¿Qué tiene su hijo?

2. Mi hijo es un jugador de fútbol, un gran jugador de fútbol.

3. Y luego sentí un dolor muy fuerte en la pierna derecha.

4. Tus ojos parecen normales, pero creo que es mejor que te observamos esta noche.

5. ¿Cuándo podemos pasar a buscarlo?

6. Y... ¿no va a poder andar?

7. Y no se preocupe, señora.

B. ¡A contestar! Indica la letra de la palabra o la frase que mejor completa cada oración según el video.

1. El doctor viene _____.

   a. tranquilo **b.** por el pasillo

2. José Luis durmió _____ anoche.

   a. muy poco **b.** mucho

3. El doctor tiene que examinar _____.

   a. al paciente **b.** los detalles

4. A José Luis le duele muchísimo _____.

   a. la cabeza **b.** la pierna

5. Parece que tiene _____.

   a. un brazo roto **b.** una pierna rota

6. Necesita pasar _____ en el hospital.

   a. la noche **b.** dos noches

7. Al principio debe guardar cama. Y luego va a necesitar _____.

   a. comer algo ligero **b.** andar con muletas

C. Ventana cultural: ¿Yo u otra persona? In the video you heard the doctor, José Luis, and José Luis' parents referring to themselves and to others. Mark an **X** in the appropriate box to indicate to whom each sentence refers.

	Yo	Otra persona
1. Puede explicarme la situación.	☐	☐
2. ¿Te sigue doliendo?	☐	☐
3. Me duele muchísimo.	☐	☐
4. ¿Te duelen los brazos?	☐	☐
5. Es mejor que te observemos esta noche.	☐	☐
6. La enfermera le pidió algo ligero.	☐	☐

LECCIÓN 3

PARA EMPEZAR

To play **Para empezar** from start to finish, use barcode or counter:

| 13:53 | – | 17:43 |

Side 7, 24996 to 31877

A. Los regalos. Mientras escuchas el video, haz una línea de cada regalo a la persona que le dio el regalo a José Luis.

1. una foto   **a.** Rita

2. una revista de deportes   **b.** Rubén

3. un ramo de flores   **c.** Silvia

4. una bata   **d.** Alfredo

5. bombones   **e.** Carla

6. un trofeo   **f.** El entrenador

7. una zapatilla   **g.** Paco

B. ¿Cierto o falso? Indica con un círculo si estas oraciones son
C (ciertas) o **F (falsas)** según el video.

C   F   **1.** Todos los amigos de José Luis le traen regalos.

C   F   **2.** Rubén va a poner la revista sobre el escritorio.

C   F   **3.** El estante está cubierto con flores.

C   F   **4.** Su amigo Alfredo va a darle una zapatilla para su cumpleaños.

C   F   **5.** Carla pone la bata nueva en el armario.

C   F   **6.** El trofeo es en broma.

C   F   **7.** Es un trofeo para el jugador más atlético del partido.

C. Ventana cultural: ¡Pobre José Luis! Since José Luis has a broken
leg, his friends have brought him many gifts. Mark with an **X** any gifts that
were given to José Luis by his friends.

☐	flores	☐	un trofeo
☐	una bata	☐	un libro
☐	una revista	☐	zapatillas
☐	una pelota	☐	tarjetas
☐	bombones	☐	televisor

Which of the gifts would you give to a friend with a broken leg? Are there
any other gifts that you might give?

_____

¿QUÉ DECIMOS...?

A. ¿Sí o no? Mientras escuchas el video, indica con una **X** si las respuestas a estas preguntas son **Sí** o **No**.

To play **¿Qué decimos?** from start to finish, use barcode or counter:

17:44 – 20:37

Side 7, 31904 to 37100

	Sí	No
1. ¿Está la cama demasiado lejos de la ventana?	☐	☐
2. ¿Ponen la mesita al lado de la cama?	☐	☐
3. ¿Está la lámpara encima de la mesa?	☐	☐
4. ¿Debe de estar allí en el estante el televisor?	☐	☐
5. ¿Ponen el sillón cerca de la mesita para las visitas?	☐	☐
6. ¿Están las zapatillas debajo del estante, como siempre?	☐	☐
7. ¿Está la bata sobre el sillón?	☐	☐

B. ¡Qué conmoción! ¿Qué dicen los padres de José Luis mientras reorganizan su cuarto? Marca con un círculo la palabra que mejor completa sus comentarios según el video.

1. La cama está demasiado (cerca, lejos) del baño

2. Ahora, pon la mesita (al lado, encima) de la cama.

3. ¡Ten cuidado con la lámpara que está (encima, debajo) de la mesa!

4. Y ahora pon el sillón más (lejos, cerca) de la cama.

5. Las zapatillas están (encima, debajo) de la cama, como siempre.

6. La bata está (sobre, al lado de) el sillón.

C. El fútbol. You can learn more soccer vocabulary by listening to Alfredo and José Luis. Unscramble the letters below to form soccer words.

1. tradipo _____

2. pratema _____

3. qualbore _____

4. querrao _____

D. Ventana cultural: Mandatos. In the video, you heard people giving orders to other people. Can you identify which of the following sentences are orders or commands? Write **M (mandato)** before each order or command.

_____ Pon la mesita al lado de la cama.

_____ Ten cuidado con la lámpara.

_____ Abre la ventana.

_____ Ven acá.

_____ Ve a la cocina.

With a partner, practice telling each other to open the book and to put it in various places.

UNIDAD 8

CULTURAL MONTAGE:
Segovia, España

To play the montage, use barcode or counter:

| 20:43 | – | 21:25 |

Side 8, 10 to 1265

1. a. Why do you think there are so many old structures in Segovia?

_____

_____

_____

b. Do you think Segovia is proud of its ancient heritage? Why?

_____

_____

_____

2. This aqueduct was built by the Romans.

a. What is the purpose of an aqueduct?

_____

_____

_____

b. Aqueducts are not used much any more. Do you know why? What is the source of water for your city? Discuss these questions with two classmates and tell the class your conclusions.

L E C C I Ó N   1

PARA EMPEZAR

To play **Para empezar** from start to finish, use barcode or counter:

| 21:26 | – | 25:23 |

Side 8, 1299 to 8427

A. ¿Sí o no? Mira y escucha el video. Luego indica si la respuesta correcta a estas preguntas es **Sí** o **No**.

1. ¿Va Marta a una fiesta en casa de su amiga Inés esta tarde?   Sí   No

2. ¿Se levanta Marta rápidamente y va a su cuarto?   Sí   No

3. Mientras se seca el pelo, ¿se quita Tere la ropa para bañarse?   Sí   No

4. ¿Marta se pinta en su cuarto?   Sí   No

5. ¿Se pone Marta su nueva blusa azul?   Sí   No

6. ¿Entra Marta en la sala para despedirse de su mamá?   Sí   No

7. ¿Quiere decirle Tere que hay una fiesta mañana?   Sí   No

8. ¿Está Inés enferma?   Sí   No

B. Orden numérico. Enumera estas actividades en el orden en que ocurren en el video.

a. _____   Marta entra en la cocina para despedirse de su madre.

b. _____   Se lava los dientes.

c. _____   Marta está durmiendo la siesta.

d. _____   Se quita la ropa para bañarse.

e. _____   Se levanta y se mira en el espejo.

f. _____   Marta se levanta lentamente y va a su cuarto.

g. _____   Se sienta frente al espejo y se peina.

C. ¿Qué dice? Mientras escuchas el video, selecciona la letra de la palabra
o la frase que completa cada oración.

1. Esta tarde Marta va a una fiesta en casa de su amiga _____.

   a. Tere   **b.** Inés

2. La fiesta es a las _____.

   a. seis   **b.** siete

3. Todavía tiene que _____.

   a. arreglarle   **b.** levantarle

4. Marta _____ y se lava el pelo.

   a. se quita   **b.** se baña

5. Tere empieza a _____ también

   a. pintarse   **b.** peinarse

6. Mamá tiene todo para la _____.

   a. fiesta   **b.** excursión

7. ¡Tere! ¿Qué quieres? ¡Tengo_____!

   a. prisa   **b.** hambre

D. Ventana cultural: La comida. En el video, los Molina van a ir a Segovia.

1. ¿Qué van a preparar para la excursión?

_____

_____

_____

2. ¿Qué van a comer los Molina para el desayuno?

_____

_____

_____

¿QUÉ DECIMOS...?

A. La familia Molina. Mientras miras y escuchas el video, marca con una **X** todas las actividades de Andrés y su hermana Marta.

Un día muy especial: Andrés

☐ se acuesta muy tarde

☐ se viste lentamente

☐ se lava los dientes

☐ se levanta inmediatamente

☐ corre

☐ se pone el reloj

Ya me levanto: Marta

☐ se levanta rápidamente

☐ se lava el pelo

☐ se quita la ropa y se baña

☐ se afeita

☐ se pinta

☐ se arregla inmediatamente

B. Un día especial. Hoy no es un día típico en la vida de los Molina. ¿Por qué? Indica con un círculo la palabra que completa cada descripción de un día especial en la vida de los Molina.

1. Esta mañana (Tere, Marta) tiene que secarse el pelo.

2. Van de excursión a (Madrid, Segovia).

3. Marta tiene que darse prisa porque su (pan tostado / chocolate) se va a enfriar.

4. (Papá, Andrés) quiere un poco de café.

5. (Marta, Tere) corta el chorizo.

6. (Marta, Tere) trae la mayonesa de la nevera.

7. (Marta, Mamá) prepara los bocadillos.

8. (Marta, Tere) cuenta los cubiertos.

C. ¿Quién? Haz una línea de cada oración a la foto de la persona que hace lo que dice la oración.

1. Se despierta muy temprano y se levanta inmediatamente.

2. Se pone el reloj y sale a correr.

3. No puede entrar en el baño porque papá todavía está afeitándose.

4. Tiene que secarse el pelo.

5. Toma sólo un poco de café.

6. Ya tiene la tortilla y el chorizo.

Marta

papá

mamá

Andrés

D. Ventana cultural: El desayuno. In the video, you saw the Molina family having breakfast. Do you think they were eating a typical breakfast? What were they eating and drinking?

_____

_____

_____

_____

Do you have any of these things for breakfast? Ask several classmates what they eat and drink at breakfast. Do you have any of the same things?

LECCIÓN 2

To play **Para empezar** from start to finish, use barcode or counter:

| 30:24 | – | 34:22 |

Side 8, 17413 to 24575

PARA EMPEZAR

A. El hotel. Mientras escuchas el video, marca con una **X** todos los cuartos del hotel que se mencionan.

☐ el baño   ☐ la habitación

☐ el comedor   ☐ el garaje

☐ el pasillo   ☐ el salón de entrada

☐ la sala de casa

B. ¿Qué dice? ¿Cómo describe Tere el hotel? Señala con un círculo la palabra que mejor completa cada oración.

1. Se sienta en una silla (muy grande, elegante).

2. No le gusta la silla porque es (demasiado, un poco) dura.

3. Todos los muebles son (viejísimos, elegantísimos).

4. Unos parecen más cómodos, otros menos cómodos, pero todos son (impresionantes, muy caros).

5. El comedor es (grandísimo, precioso).

C. Ventana cultural: El hotel. Following the Molina family around the Hotel Infanta Isabel, you saw all of the items listed below. Indicate with an **X** which items give clues that the hotel is located in Spain.

☐ la recepción   ☐ el espejo

☐ los muebles   ☐ los letreros

☐ el comedor   ☐ la vista

☐ la habitación   ☐ el pasillo

With a classmate, discuss why you marked specific items.

VIDEO WORKSHEETS ¡DIME! UNO

¿QUÉ DECIMOS...?

A. Descripciones. Mientras escuchas el video, marca con una **X** todas las palabras que los miembros de la familia Molina usan para describir la comida del almuerzo.

☐ sabrosos   ☐ fría   ☐ riquísima   ☐ fantásticos

☐ sin sabor   ☐ malísima   ☐ buena   ☐ terrible

Ahora marca con una **X** todas las palabras que los miembros de la familia Molina usan para describir el Alcázar de Segovia.

☐ impresionante   ☐ increíbles   ☐ bonitos   ☐ blanda

☐ feos   ☐ grandísima   ☐ interesantes   ☐ bellísima

☐ elegantísima   ☐ cómodos   ☐ duros   ☐ viejísimos

B. ¿Sí o no? Mientras escuchas el video, indica si las respuestas a estas preguntas son **Sí** o **No**.

	Sí	No
1. ¿Le gustó a papá la ensaladilla rusa?	☐	☐
2. ¿La encontró buena Andrés?	☐	☐
3. ¿Hay algo de postre?	☐	☐
4. ¿Es grandísima la sala de la galera?	☐	☐
5. ¿Parecen cómodos los tronos de los Reyes?	☐	☐
6. ¿Se permite tocar los muebles?	☐	☐
7. ¿Subieron ciento cuarenta escalones a la torre?	☐	☐

C. Ventana cultural: El Alcázar. **El Alcázar** is an imposing landmark in Segovia. After accompanying the Molina family on the tour of the **Alcázar**, why do you think this is an important historical place? What clues did you see in the video?

_____

_____

_____

If you were to visit the Alcázar, what part would you particularly like to see?

la sala de galera   _____   los tronos de los reyes _____

el dormitorio del rey _____   la torre   _____

Explain your choice to a classmate.

LECCIÓN 3

To play **Para empezar** from start to finish, use barcode or counter:

| 38:26 | – | 44:02 |

Side 8, 31877 to 41950

PARA EMPEZAR

A. Primero... Carlos Sartén es un famoso cocinero. ¿Puedes entender sus instrucciones? Enumera de uno a cinco en orden cronológico los pasos que tomó para preparar la tortilla y las albondiguitas.

La tortilla española

_____   Hay que darle la vuelta.

_____   Mezcla todo con seis huevos y sal.

_____   Fríe tres patatas cortadas y una cebolla.

_____   Hay que pasarla a la sartén y luego al fuego unos minutos más.

_____   Se deja freír lentamente.

Albondiguitas

_____   Se mezcla la carne con el pan, los huevos, el ajo y el perejil.

_____   En una sartén se fríen lentamente con aceite de oliva.

_____   Se corta la carne.

_____   Se hacen bolitas con la mezcla.

_____   Se pica la carne.

B. ¿Cierto o falso? ¿Cómo es Carlos Sartén y qué hace? Indica si estas descripciones son **C** (**ciertas**) o **F** (**falsas**).

C   F   **1.** Carlos Sartén es un cocinero famosísimo.

C   F   **2.** Es el cocinero más serio del mundo.

C   F   **3.** Es organizado y sus recetas son realmente fabulosas.

C   F   **4.** ¡Se corta el dedo!

C   F   **5.** Quema la tortilla.

C   F   **6.** Es muy cómico, pero qué desastre.

C. ¿Qué dice? Mientras escuchas el video, escribe la palabra apropiada que completa la oración.

cocinero   cuidado   desastre   exquisita

el perejil   recetas   tamaño   tapas

1. Tiene que ser el _____ más cómico del mundo.

2. Hoy vamos a preparar dos_____.

3. Sus _____ son realmente fabulosas.

4. Se mezcla la carne con el pan, los huevos, el ajo y _____.

5. Todas las albóndigas son del mismo _____, ¿Eh?

6. ¡Tengan _____ de no quemar las albóndigas!

7. Tendrán una tortilla _____ y unas albondiguitas fenomenales.

8. Es muy cómico, pero qué _____.

D. Ventana cultural: ¿Tortilla o albondiguitas? Mientras escuchas
el video, identifica los ingredientes de una tortilla y de las albondiguitas.
Marca con una **T** (**tortilla**) todos los ingredientes de la tortilla y con una **A**
(**albondiguitas**) todos los de las albondiguitas. Algunos ingredientes se
usan en ambas.

_____ patatas	_____ huevos	_____ carne
_____ cebolla	_____ queso	_____ sal
_____ pimienta	_____ pan	_____ aceite de oliva
_____ jamón	_____ perejil	_____ ajo

¿QUÉ DECIMOS...?

To play **¿Qué decimos?** from start to finish, use barcode or counter:

Side 8, 41972 to 50153

A. En Segovia. ¿Qué comentan los miembros de la familia Molina mientras miran el acueducto de Segovia. Haz una línea de cada comentario a la foto de la persona que hizo el comentario.

1. ¡Qué impresionante es el acueducto!

2. Lo construyeron los romanos en el siglo primero o segundo después de Jesucristo.

3. No utilizaron ni mortero ni cemento.

4. ¿Por qué lo construyeron?

5. Recuerdo cuando todavía traía agua a la ciudad.

6. Es fascinante.

B. En el restaurante. Mientras escuchas el video, selecciona la letra de la palabra o la frase que completa cada oración.

1. Buenas tardes. ¿Tiene una mesa _____?
   a. construida   **b.** reservada

2. Sí, mira los adornos. Son _____.
   a. perfecta   **b.** preciosos

3. A ver, queremos _____, ¿no?
   a. tortilla española   **b.** cochinillo asado

4. Mejor pedimos _____.
   a. los entremeses variados   **b.** un bocadillo

5. Muy bien. Y de _____ plato, ¿qué desean?
   a. segundo   **b.** primer

6. ¿Cómo puedo comer el cochinillo si me está _____?
   a. sonriendo   **b.** hablando

C. Ventana cultural: El cochinillo asado. In the video, you saw the family order a meal for which the restaurant is famous. Would you like to try the meal that the Molinas ordered? With a partner discuss why or why not. Which of the foods mentioned in the video would you most like to try?

LECCIÓN PRELIMINAR

PARA EMPEZAR

A. Orden numérico.
- **a.** 1
- **b.** 3
- **c.** 2

B. Detective.

Clase
mochila, pizarra, pupitre,
escritorio de profesor, mesa, silla, tiza,
borrador

Mochila
lápiz, bolígrafo, carpeta, cuaderno

Escritorio
libro de español, bolígrafo, carpeta
cuaderno, lápiz, regla

C. Ventana cultural: Dos culturas.
Answers will vary, but most items can be
found in both classrooms.

¿QUÉ DECIMOS...?

A. ¿Qué hay en la lista?
un cuaderno, un lápiz, un bolígrafo,
papel, una carpeta

B. Ventana cultural: Dos culturas.
Answers will vary.

UNIDAD 1

CULTURAL MONTAGE

Answers will vary.

LECCIÓN 1

PARA EMPEZAR

A. Saludos y despedidas.
1. Srta. Montero and Lupe, S
2. Beto and Lupe, D
3. Ana and Beto, S
4. Sr. Ramos and Andrés, S
5. Jaime and Beto, D

B. ¿Quiénes son?
- **a.** Ana
- **b.** Beto
- **c.** Sr. Whitaker
- **d.** Srta. Montero
- **e.** Sra. León
- **f.** Sr. Ramos
- **g.** Andrés

C. ¡Hola!
1. un besito
2. darse la mano
3. un besito
4. darse la mano
5. darse la mano

D. ¿Qué dice?
1. estudiante
2. español
3. profesor
4. amiga
5. director

¿QUÉ DECIMOS...?

A. ¿Cómo estás?
- **a.** Srta. Montero, 5
- **b.** Lupe, 1
- **c.** Andrés, 7
- **d.** Beto, 2
- **e.** Sr. Whitaker, 6
- **f.** Sr. Ramos, 4
- **g.** Ana, 3

B. ¡A contestar!

1. b   4. c
2. d   5. a
3. e

C. ¡A charlar!

1. soy
2. gusto
3. Qué tal
4. usted
5. Encantada
6. Hasta mañana

D. ¿Qué tal?

1. ¿Cómo está usted?
2. ¿Cómo estás?
3. ¿Cómo está usted?
4. ¿Cómo está usted?
5. ¿Cómo estás?
6. ¿Cómo estás?
7. ¿Cómo estás?

LECCIÓN 2

PARA EMPEZAR

A. Soy de Ecuador.

1. Srta. Montero
2. Jaime
3. Pilar
4. Sr. Ramos

B. Mucho gusto.

1. Mucho gusto
2. Iqualmente
3. Es un placer
4. Mucho gusto

C. ¿Presentarle o presentarte?

1. presentarle
2. presentarte
3. presentarte
4. presentarle
5. presentarle
6. presentarte

¿QUÉ DECIMOS...?

A. Silvia es de Ecuador.

1. M
2. S
3. A
4. D
5. R
6. D
7. B

B. Quiero presentarte...

1. a. Srta. Montero
   b. David
   c. Silvia
2. a. Ana
   b. Silvia
3. a. David
   b. Silvia
   c. Sr. Ramos

C. Mucho gusto

1. Encantado, preciosa.
2. Mucho gusto.
3. Mucho gusto.
4. Encantado, preciosa.
5. Answers will vary.
6. Encantado, preciosa.
7. Mucho gusto.
8. Mucho gusto.

LECCIÓN 3

PARA EMPEZAR

A. ¿Alta o baja?

Answers include morena, rubia, bonita, cómica, alta, baja, mediana, delgada, atlética, tímida, popular, inteligente.

B. ¿Quién es?

1. Ángela
2. Gloria
3. Ángela
4. Jaime
5. Carlos
6. Pirata

C. ¿Cómo es?

Carmen: morena, baja, inteligente
Jaime: moreno, estudioso, alto, guapo, elegante
Pirata: popular, feo, bajo, tonto, gordo, simpático

D. Ventana cultural: ¿Masculino o femenino?

Jaime: guapo, alto, estudioso, moreno, delgado
Ángela: morena, delgada, atlética, bonita, alta

¿QUE DECIMOS...?

A. Es muy guapo.

1. Beto
2. Jaime
3. Ana
4. Jaime
5. Lupe
6. Beto
7. Jaime

B. ¡Entrevista!

1. flaco
2. popular
3. simpática
4. modesta
5. guapo
6. tonto

C. ¿Cómo es?

Answers will vary.

D. Ventana Cultural: Estudiantes de dos escuelas.

1. Esteban and Jaime
2. Sara and Ana
3. Esteban and Jaime
4. Sara and Ana
5. Esteban and Jaime
6. Sara and Ana
7. Sara and Ana
8. Esteban and Jaime

UNIDAD 2

CULTURAL MONTAGE

1. Answers will vary.
2. a. Answers will vary but should refer to the flags of Puerto Rico and the United States of America.
   b. Answers will vary but should include a reference to Puerto Rico being a U.S. territory.
3. Answers will vary.

LECCIÓN 1

PARA EMPEZAR

A. ¿Qué clase tiene?

1. química
2. educación física
3. historia
4. español
5. inglés

B. Las clases.
1. Sara, Raúl
2. Esteban
3. Sara
4. Sara, Raúl
5. Sara, Mónica

C. ¿A qué hora?
1. 9:05
2. 10:30
3. 1:00
4. 1:45
5. 7:00

D. Ventana cultural: Dos escuelas.
Answers will vary.

¿QUÉ DECIMOS...?

A. ¿Qué dice?
1. sí
2. sí
3. no
4. sí
5. no
6. sí

B. ¿Cuándo?
1. c
2. a
3. b
4. d

C. ¿Qué pasa?
1. a
2. a
3. b
4. b
5. b

D. Ventana cultural: Números de teléfono.
Answers will vary.

LECCIÓN 2

PARA EMPEZAR

A. La escuela Robinson.
a. 5, **b.** 2, **c.** 4, **d.** 1, **e.** 3

B. ¿Cómo es la escuela?
1. fantástico
2. divertida
3. divertido
4. nuevos
5. inteligentes
6. díficiles
7. serios, exigentes

C. Mi escuela.
Answers will vary.

D. Ventana cultural: Las escuelas.
Answers will vary.

¿QUÉ DECIMOS...?

A. La escuela Robinson.
1. P
2. P
3. C
4. P
5. P
6. C
7. P
8. C

B. ¡A charlar!
1. **a.** gimnasio
   b. biblioteca
2. **a.** fáciles
   b. excelentes
3. **a.** Matemáticas
   b. desorganizada
4. **a.** historia
   b. perfeccionista

C. Ventana cultural:
¿Una persona o dos?

1. dos personas
2. una persona
3. dos personas
4. una persona
5. una persona
6. dos personas

LECCIÓN 3

PARA EMPEZAR

A. ¿Qué hacen?
All activities should be marked except **escribir cartas, ver la tele, beber un refresco**, and **jugar tenis**.

B. Las actividades.

1. calificar
2. hablar
3. jugar
4. comer
5. limpiar
6. alquilar

C. ¿Quién hace la actividad?

1. Tomás
2. Sr. Arenas
3. Tomás
4. Carmen
5. Sr. Arenas
6. Tomás
7. Tomás

D. Ventana cultural: Actividades.
Answers will vary.

¿QUÉ DECIMOS...?

A. ¿Quién?

1. Sara
2. Mónica
3. Carmen
4. Sra. Estrada

5. Tomás
6. Raúl
7. Carlos

B. ¿Actividad o obligación?

1. O
2. A
3. O
4. A
5. A
6. O
7. A
8. A

C. ¿Y el profesor?
Answers will vary.

D. Tus actividades
Answers will vary.

E. Ventana cultural: Letreros.

1. Meaning: bus stop; sketches will vary.
2. Meaning: school zone; 25 miles per hour, sketches will vary.

UNIDAD 3

CULTURAL MONTAGE

1. Answers will vary but may include reference to the taxis being yellow Volkswagen Beetles.
2. Answers will vary.

LECCIÓN 1

PARA EMPEZAR

A. Lugares importantes.
1. centros comerciales
2. monumento
3. la plaza
4. teatro
5. parque
6. tiendas

B. ¿Cómo es?
Answers will vary. The following are sample answers.
1. es la avenida más importante de la ciudad.
2. es la plaza principal. Aquí está la Catedral.
3. es un teatro muy importante.
4. es el parque más grande de la capital.
5. es una zona comercial. Hay tiendas elegantes, excelentes restaurantes y cafés al aire libre.

C. Ventana cultural: Lugares importantes.
Answers will vary.

¿QUÉ DECIMOS...?

A. ¿Quién es?
1. Daniel   4. Riqui
2. Alicia   5. Mamá
3. Kati   6. Papá

B. ¿Cierto o falso?
1. C   4. F
2. C   5. F
3. F   6. C

C. ¡A charlar!
1. Kati   3. papá
2. mamá   4. Daniel

D. Ventana cultural: El sábado.
1. going to the park
2. Answers will vary but may refer to being an activity for the whole family.
3. Answers will vary.

LECCIÓN 2

PARA EMPEZAR

A. ¿Cuándo?
1. F   4. F
2. C   5. C
3. C

B. El tiempo en la Ciudad de México.
1. a   4. d
2. b   5. c
3. a, b

C. Ventana cultural: El Bosque de Chapultepec.
1. Answers will vary.
2. Answers will vary.
3. el Museo de Antropología
4. visitar el Museo de Antropología, mirar los animales, subir a la montaña rusa, subir a las lanchas, correr
5. Answers will vary.

¿QUÉ DECIMOS...?

A. ¿Qué hace?
Answers will vary but may include **pasear, leer el periódico, escuchar la radio, descansar, tomar un refresco, escribir una carta, mirar a la gente, subir a las lanchas, visitar el Museo de Antropología, visitar el jardin zoológico, comprar helado, ir al parque de diversiones, subir a la montaña rusa, subir al carusel, subir a los carros chocones.**

B. ¿Qué dice?
1. Riqui
2. Pedro Solís
3. Eloísa Miramontes
4. Riqui
5. Eloísa Miramontes
6. Daniel

C. ¿Yo?
1. otra persona
2. yo
3. yo
4. otra persona
5. otra persona
6. yo
7. otra persona

D. Ventana cultural: ¿Adulto o chico?
Answers will vary.

LECCIÓN 3

PARA EMPEZAR

A. Un fin de semana típico.
1. b
2. b
3. a
4. a

B. ¿Viernes, sábado o domingo?
1. D
2. V
3. V
4. S
5. S
6. D
7. S

C. Ventana cultural: El fin de semana.
Answers will vary.

¿QUÉ DECIMOS...?

A. ¿Sí o no?
1. Sí
2. No
3. Sí
4. Sí
5. No
6. No
7. No

B. ¿Dónde?
1. centro comercial
2. fiesta
3. restaurante
4. centro comercial
5. restaurante
6. restaurante
7. centro comercial
8. restaurante

C. ¿Quién?
1. Kati
2. Daniel
3. Daniel
4. Alicia
5. Kati
6. Daniel

D. Ventana cultural: ¿México o EE.UU.?
Answers will vary.

UNIDAD 4

CULTURAL MONTAGE
1. Answers will vary.
2. Answers will vary but should include some reference to Texas having once been a part of Mexico.
3. Answers will vary but may include a reference to the siege of the Alamo or the deaths of Jim Bowie and William Travis.

LECCIÓN 1

PARA EMPEZAR

A. ¿Quién es?

back row: Rafael, Betty, Kevin
next row: Elena, Sarita, Paquito
next row: Margarita, Patricio, Lupe
front row: Roberto, Pepe, Ana

B. ¿Cuántos años?

Ana   16
Rafael   44
Paquito   9
Lupe   13
Patricio   68
Pepe   6
Sarita   8
Kevin   17

C. La familia.

1. h   **6.** i
2. a   **7.** f
3. g   **8.** d
4. c   **9.** e
5. b

D. ¿Cuántos años?

1. cuarenta y cuatro
2. sesenta y ocho
3. diecisiete
4. diecinueve
5. treinta
6. doce

E. Ventana cultural: Los cumpleaños.

Answers will vary.

¿QUÉ DECIMOS…?

A. Hola, tía.

1. 17   **5.** mis sobrinos
2. sesenta y ocho   **6.** pequeños
3. tía Elena   **7.** San Antonio de Padua
4. mis hijos

B. ¿Qué dice?

1. Patricio
2. Elena
3. Lupe
4. Rafael
5. Betty
6. Rafael, Betty

C. Ventana cultural: El cumpleaños.

1. ¡Feliz cumpleaños!
2. ¡Felicidades!

LECCIÓN 2

PARA EMPEZAR

A. ¿De veras?

1. Sí   **5.** Sí
2. No   **6.** Sí
3. No   **7.** Sí
4. No   **8.** No

B. ¿Quién es?

1. Mario   **6.** Lola
2. Juliana   **7.** Elvira
3. Lola   **8.** Mario
4. Kevin   **9.** Juliana
5. Betty

C. Es futbolista.

1. Juliana   **4.** Lola
2. Diego   **5.** Betty
3. Mario

D. Ventana cultural: Las profesiones.

Answers will vary.

¿QUÉ DECIMOS…?

A. Conversaciones.

1. a. Julio, b. Kevin
2. a. Julio, b. Kevin
3. a. Juliana, b. Paquito
4. a. Julio, b. Kevin

B. ¿Quién?

1. Rafael
2. Paquito
3. Elvira
4. Juliana
5. Paquito
6. Rafael
7. Kevin
8. Pamela

C. Ventana cultural: La recepción.

punch, relatives, musicians, food, dancing, photographer, eating, wedding cake, flowers; Answers will vary.

LECCIÓN 3

PARA EMPEZAR

A. ¿Cierto o falso?

1.	C	5.	F
2.	F	6.	C
3.	F	7.	C
4.	C		

B. ¿Qué dice?

1. lista
2. emocionadas
3. ridículas
4. bailando
5. furioso
6. suerte
7. bebiendo
8. hablando

C. Ventana cultural: ¿Opinión o sentimiento?

1.	S	6.	O
2.	S	7.	S
3.	O, S	8.	S
4.	O	9.	S
5.	S	10.	O

¿QUÉ DECIMOS...?

A. ¿Quién?

1. a
2. b
3. c
4. a
5. b
6. b
7. a
8. c
9. b
10. b

B. Es tan guapo.

1. Pamela
2. Kevin, Julio
3. Betty, Rafael
4. Leslie
5. Kevin
6. Julio
7. Leslie
8. Betty, Rafael
9. Pamela
10. Julio

C. Ventana cultural: Expresiones.

1, 2, 3, 4, 5, 6, 8, 9

UNIDAD 5

CULTURAL MONTAGE

Answers will vary.

LECCIÓN 1

PARA EMPEZAR

A. ¿A la izquierda?

The routes are the same as in the text.

B. Dobla a la derecha.
1. Enrique
2. Mariseta
3. Carla
4. Luis

C Ventana cultural: Las calles.
1. Calle Goya, Calle Reina, Calle Clavel, Calle Alcalá, Calle del Conde
2. Answers will vary.

¿QUÉ DECIMOS...?

A. Al pedir instrucciones.
a. 5
b. 3
c. 1
d. 2
e. 4

B. ¿Quién dice esto?

1.	b	5.	e
2.	c	6.	d
3.	a	7.	b
4.	e		

C. Una familia argentina.

1.	a	4.	b
2.	b	5.	b
3.	b		

D. Ventana cultural: Manolo es de Argentina.

The word **manzanas** is the equivilant of **cuadras.**

LECCIÓN 2

PARA EMPEZAR

A. ¿Qué prefiere?
unos jeans, una camiseta amarilla, unos zapatos deportivos, una sudadera gris, unos pantalones grises, unos calcetines azules

B. ¿Qué dice?
1. sombreros
2. vestido
3. traje
4. camisetas
5. pantalones
6. calcetines
7. blusa
8. sudadera

C. Ventana cultural: ¡De compras!
Answers will vary.

¿QUÉ DECIMOS...?

A. ¿Cierto o falso?

1.	C	6.	F
2.	F	7.	C
3.	C	8.	C
4.	F	9.	F
5.	C		

B. ¿Qué les gusta?
una camiseta roja, una camiseta amarilla, una camiseta azul, unos zapatos, una camisa roja

C. ¿Qué dice?
1. Víctor
2. Manolo
3. Víctor
4. Manolo
5. Manolo
6. Víctor
7. Víctor

D. Ventana cultural: El almacén.
1. camisas
2. zapatos
3. sombreros
4. perfume
5. frutería
6. lechería

LECCIÓN 3

PARA EMPEZAR

A. ¿Qué pedimos?

café con leche, agua mineral sin gas, melón, hamburguesa, refresco, sándwich mixto, bocadillo de jamón serrano, limonada, bizcocho, perrito

B. ¿Qué dice?

1.	b	5.	b
2.	a	6.	a
3.	c	7.	b
4.	c	8.	a

C. Ventana cultural: La comida.

1. manzanas, naranjas, melón
2. A **bocadillo** is made with a roll. A **sándwich** is made with sliced bread.

¿QUÉ DECIMOS...?

A. ¿Quiénes?

1. Víctor
2. Víctor
3. Víctor, Manolo
4. papá
5. camarero
6. Víctor
7. Manolo
8. mamá, papá, Manolo, Víctor
9. mamá
10. camarero
11. papá
12. Manolo
13. papá, Manolo, Víctor
14. Víctor
15. Manolo
16. mamá
17. Víctor
18. papá
19. papá
20. camarero

B. ¿Qué piden?

Papá
sándwich mixto, agua mineral

Mamá
bizcocho, café con leche

Víctor
hamburguesa, papas fritas

Manolo
melón, limonada

C. Respuestas.

1. f
2. d
3. j
4. i
5. a
6. h
7. e
8. b

UNIDAD 6

CULTURAL MONTAGE

1. a. Answers will vary but may include reference to old government buildings, a theater and old or original buildings of the city.
   b. Answers will vary.
2. papier-mâché bird, clay figures
3. Answers will vary.

LECCIÓN 1

PARA EMPEZAR

A. ¿Quién lo hace?

1. Mamá
2. Óscar
3. Mónica
4. Óscar
5. Mónica
6. Óscar

B. ¿Qué pasó?

a. 6
b. 1
c. 4
d. 7
e. 5
f. 2
g. 8
h. 3

C. Ventana cultural: ¿Adónde fueron?

1. la Plaza de los Mariachis
2. el Mercado Libertad
3. el Teatro Degollado
4. el Palacio de Gobierno

Answers will vary.

¿QUÉ DECIMOS...?

A. ¡Estupendo!

romántica, riquísima, contenta, simpáticos, linda, pequeño, divertido, impresionante, enorme, bonitas, hermosísima, guapo

B. ¿Qué dice?

1. recibieron
2. llevó
3. decidieron
4. compré
5. pagaron

C. ¿Quiénes?

1. Lilia
2. Lilia, Mónica
3. Óscar, Javier
4. Mónica
5. Óscar, Javier

D. Ventana cultural: El mercado.

Answers will vary.

PARA EMPEZAR

A. ¿Quién es?

1. Óscar
2. Toño
3. Óscar
4. Mónica
5. Mónica
6. Óscar
7. Óscar
8. Toño

B. Respuestas.

1. b
2. b
3. a
4. a
5. b

C. Ventana cultural: Las artesanías.

1. c
2. a
3. b

¿QUÉ DECIMOS...?

A. ¿Cierto o falso?

1. F
2. C
3. F
4. C
5. C
6. F
7. F
8. F
9. C
10. C

B. ¿Qué dice?

1. c   4. b
2. b   5. b
3. a   6. a

C. Ventana Cultural: Las artesanías.

Answers will vary.

© McDougal Littell, Inc.

LECCIÓN 3

PARA EMPEZAR

A. ¿Quién es?

1. I		**5.** I
2. R		**6.** P
3. I		**7.** P
4. P		**8.** I, P

B. Ventana cultural: Las leyendas.

Answers will vary.

¿QUÉ DECIMOS...?

A. ¿Cierto o falso?

1. F		**6.** C
2. C		**7.** C
3. F		**8.** C
4. F		**9.** F
5. F		

B. ¿Qué dice?

1. regresaste
2. tuvimos
3. pensé
4. busqué
5. empezó
6. dejaste
7. contaron

C. ¿Sí o no?

1. Sí		**5.** No
2. No		**6.** Sí
3. Sí		**7.** Sí
4. No		**8.** No

D. Ventana cultural: ¡Qué héroe!

Answers will vary.

UNIDAD 7

CULTURAL MONTAGE

1. **a.** Miami is in Florida, a peninsula.
   b. Answers wil vary.
   c. Answers will vary.
2. **a.** There is a large Cuban population in Miami.
   b. Calle Ocho, La Prada Cafetería, Casablanca

LECCIÓN 1

PARA EMPEZAR

A. Deportes.

a. 4		**d.** 2
b. 1		**e.** 5
c. 6		**f.** 3

B. En Miami.

1. atlética y académica
2. fútbol
3. femininos
4. primero
5. salto de altura
6. jai alai
7. historia

C. ¿Qué deporte?

Jorge Campos: jai alai
Rafaela Delgado: track
Juan Colón: soccer
Samuel Rodríguez: track
Paula Wilson: track

D. Ventana cultural: Deportes.

jai alai; Adjectives will vary.

¿QUÉ DECIMOS...?

A. ¿Qué dice?
1. **a.** Alfredo
   b. José Luis
2. **a.** Papá
   b. Mamá
3. **a.** Mamá
   b. José Luis
   c. Papá
   d. José Luis

B. ¿A quién?

1. Alfredo	5. José Luis
2. José Luis	6. Paco
3. Paco	7. José Luis
4. José Luis	8. Mamá

C. Ventana cultural: El fútbol.

Lists should include **cabezazo, gol/meter un gol/patear un gol, pelota, defensor/defensores, árbitro.** Lists may also include **equipo, partido, entrenador, campo, falta.**

LECCIÓN 2

PARA EMPEZAR

A. ¿Qué le duele?

Answers include **la cabeza, el estómago, la pierna, el pie, los dedos el pie, el brazo, la mano.**

B. ¿Sí o No?

1. No	5. Sí
2. No	6. Sí
3. Sí	7. No
4. No	8. Sí

C. Ventana cultural: ¿María Teresa o tú?
Answers will vary.

¿QUÉ DECIMOS...?

A. ¿Qué dice?
1. el doctor
2. papá
3. José Luis
4. el doctor
5. papá
6. mamá
7. el doctor

B. ¡A contestar!

1. b	5. b
2. a	6. a
3. a	7. b
4. b	

C. Ventana cultural: ¿Yo u otra persona?
1. yo
2. otra persona
3. yo
4. otra persona
5. otra persona
6. otra persona

LECCIÓN 3

PARA EMPEZAR

A. Los regalos.

1. e	5. d
2. b	6. a
3. c	7. f
4. g	

B. ¿Cierto o falso?

1. C	5. F
2. C	6. C
3. F	7. F
4. C	

C. Ventana cultural: ¡Pobre José Luis!

Gifts include **flores, un trofeo, una bata, una revista, zapatillas, tarjetas, bombones.**

Answers will vary.

¿QUÉ DECIMOS...?

A. ¿Sí o no?

1. No		**5.** No	
2. Sí		**6.** No	
3. Sí		**7.** Sí	
4. Sí			

B. ¡Qué conmoción!

1. lejos		**4.** cerca	
2. al lado		**5.** debajo	
3. encima		**6.** sobre	

C. El fútbol.

1. partido		**3.** bloquear	
2. empatar		**4.** arquero	

D. Ventana cultural: Mandatos.

All of the sentences are commands.

UNIDAD 8

CULTURAL MONTAGE

1. **a.** Answers will vary but may include reference to Segovia being a city that had been populated by the Romans.
   b. Answers will vary.
2. **a.** An aqueduct carries water.
   b. Answers will vary.

LECCIÓN 1

PARA EMPEZAR

A. ¿Sí o no?

1. Sí		**5.** No	
2. No		**6.** Sí	
3. No		**7.** No	
4. Sí		**8.** Sí	

B. Orden numérico.

a. 7		**e.** 6	
b. 4		**f.** 2	
c. 1		**g.** 5	
d. 3			

C. ¿Qué dice?

1. b		**5.** a	
2. b		**6.** b	
3. a		**7.** a	
4. b			

D. Ventana cultural: La comida.

1. ensaladilla rusa, tortilla, bocadillos (chorizo y pan)
2. pan, mantequilla, mermelada

¿QUÉ DECIMOS...?

A. La familia Molina.

Andrés: se lava los dientes, se levanta inmediatamente, corre, se pone el reloj

Marta: se lava el pelo, se pinta

B. Un día especial.

1. Marta		**5.** Marta	
2. Segovia		**6.** Tere	
3. chocolate		**7.** Mamá	
4. Papá		**8.** Tere	

C. ¿Quién?

1. Andrés		**4.** Marta	
2. Andrés		**5.** papá	
3. Marta		**6.** mamá	

D. Ventana cultural: El desayuno.

El desayuno includes **pan, mantequilla, mermelada, chocolate, café.**
El picnic includes **tortilla, ensaladilla rusa, bocadillos.**

LECCIÓN 2

PARA EMPEZAR

A. El hotel.

el comedor, el pasillo, la habitación, el salón de entrada

B. ¿Qué dice?
1. elegante
2. demasiado
3. elegantísimos
4. impresionantes
5. precioso

C. Ventana cultural: El hotel.

Answers will vary, but **la vista** and **los letreros** should be marked.

¿QUÉ DECIMOS...?

A. Descripciones.

el almuerzo: sabrosos, riquísima, malísima, buena
el Alcázar: impresionante, increíbles, bonitos, blanda, grandísima, elegantísima, duros, viejísimos

B. ¿Sí o no?
1. Sí   5. No
2. No   6. No
3. Sí   7. Sí
4. Sí

C. Ventana cultural: El Alcázar.

Answers will vary.

LECCIÓN 3

PARA EMPEZAR

A. Primero . . .

La tortilla española: 4, 2, 1, 5, 3
Albondiguitas: 3, 5, 1, 4, 2

B. ¿Cierto o falso?
1. C   4. C
2. F   5. F
3. F   6. C

C. ¿Qué dice?
1. cocinero   5. tamaño
2. tapas   6. cuidado
3. recetas   7. exquisita
4. el perejil   8. desastre

D. Ventana cultural: ¿Tortilla o albondiguitas?

La Tortilla includes **patatas, huevos, cebolla, sal.**
Las Albondiguitas include **huevos, carne, pan, aceite de oliva, perejil, ajo.**

¿QUÉ DECIMOS...?

A. En Segovia.
1. Marta   4. Tere
2. Andrés   5. Papá
3. Andrés   6. Marta

B. En el restaurante.
1. b   4. a
2. b   5. a
3. b   6. a

C. Ventana cultural: El cochinillo asado.

Answers will vary.